Understanding, Building, and Using Baluns and Ununs

Theory and Practical Designs for the Experimenter

By Jerry Sevick, W2FMI

CQ Communications, Inc.

Library of Congress Control Number 2003103912
ISBN 0-943016-24-X

Editor: Edith Lennon, N2ZRW
Layout and Design: Elizabeth Ryan
Illustrations: Hal Keith

Published by CQ Communications, Inc.
25 Newbridge Road
Hicksville, New York 11801 USA

Printed in the United States of America.

This book is dedicated to my late wife, Connie.

Preface

I have often been asked the reason for spending so much time and effort on the transmission line transformer (TLT). It is obvious that many transformers have been constructed and measured. This whole subject resulted from a work transfer back to our Bell Labs Headquarters in Murray Hill, New Jersey, from our Western Electric Branch lab at Allentown, Pennsylvania.

Since my hobby was amateur radio, I decided to look at short vertical antennas and short radial ground systems. I found the TLT to be an ideal matching transformer for the low resonant-impedances encountered. Furthermore, my new assignment, which included arranging exchange visits between our technical staff and the outside world, gave me the opportunity to have my transformers measured on extremely

Photo 0-A. *The author's XYL sitting under the W2FMI 40-meter beach umbrella antenna.*

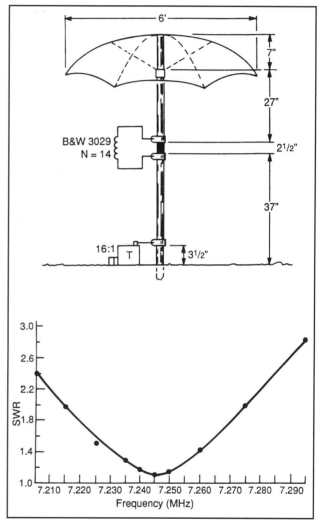

Figure 0-1. *The parameters and standing wave ratio as a function of frequency for the W2FMI 40-meter beach umbrella antenna.*

accurate transmission test sets having an error of only plus or minus 1 millidb!

The ultimate results of my studies for a short vertical antenna in the 40-meter amateur radio band appear to be for a 6-foot-tall version with a large top hat. In shopping at a sports store, I saw the beach umbrella "antenna." It was a lot of fun describing my "beach umbrella antenna" to the radio hams on the 40-meter band. **Photo 0-A** shows a view of my late wife sitting under the beach umbrella resonant in the 40-meter amateur radio band. **Figure 0-1** shows the drawing and the response curve of this interesting, short vertical antenna.

Recently I was asked by Nobel Publishing to prepare a manuscript for a video/CD ROM tutorial on my book *Transmission Line Transformers*.[1]* Looking through this book as well as my second publication *Building and Using Baluns and Ununs*[2], I found that they mainly contain the design and performance of these broadband transformers. What theory they included was dispersed throughout the books and, in reviewing all this information, I found a very simple and unified approach to presenting the theory.

Briefly it involved classifying these transformers according to impedance ratios and applying Guanella's "basic building block" in their designs. In seeking permission from CQ Communications to use some of their artwork for the tutorial, the publisher, Dick Ross, not only obliged but recommended that I update *Building and Using Baluns and Ununs*. He also suggested that I break off the appendices on "Antennas and Ground Systems" so it could stand alone under its own cover, enabling the usual Internet search engines to readily locate it. As a result the two new books will be entitled *Understanding, Building,*

and Using Baluns and Ununs and *The Short Vertical Antenna and Ground Radial*.

To understand and apply these transformers, one must be familiar with transmission line theory, conventional transformers, and general circuit theory. Graduate courses in these areas are recommended. Considerable work remains to be done on high-powered TLTs and low-impedance, low-ratio TLTs at frequencies beyond UHF.

In preparing this book I found it necessary to duplicate some of the diagrams, figures, and photos of this book in **Part II**. Since **Part I** is strictly on the theory of the broadband of the transformers, I realized that having some of the figures and photos near the explanations eliminated the chore of searching through half of the book for figures that relate to theory. The figures and photos are still necessary in **Part II**, however, which is on the building and using the TLTs.

I wish to thank four people who were instrumental in making this book possible. They are Dick Ross, Publisher, CQ Communications, Edith Lennon, Editor, and Kathy Collyer and Janette C. Bailey, my associates.

Jerry Sevick
Fellowship Village
Basking Ridge, NJ

* *There are separate References for **Parts I** and **II**. They are found at the end of each part.*

Introduction

The transmission line transformer (TLT) transmits the energy from input to output by a transmission line mode and not by flux-linkages, as in the conventional transformer. As a result, the TLT has much wider bandwidth and higher efficiencies than its conventional counterpart. With proper core materials and impedance levels of 100 ohms or less, bandwidths of about 100 MHz and efficiencies approaching 99 percent are possible today, matching 50 ohms up to 100 ohms and 50 ohms down to about 3 ohms. Future research and development, especially with impedance ratios less than 4:1, should make future TLTs operate at much wider bandwidths.

The transmission line transformer first appeared upon the scene in 1944 in a classic paper by George Guanella in the *Brown Boverie Review* (Brown Boverie is a company located in Switzerland). The title of his paper was "Novel matching systems for high frequencies."[3] The second classic paper was written by Clyde Ruthroff at Bell Labs and was published 15 years later in the *Proc. of the IRE* (Institute of Radio Engineers, which was later changed to the IEEE). His paper was fortuitously named "Some broad-band transformers."[4] In his paper he introduced the 1:4 Unun.

As seen in the **Table of Contents**, **Part I** includes a new approach to the theory of these transformers. **Chapter 3**, "TLTs with Ratios Less Than 1:4," is my contribution to the technology, and resulted from a need for a broadband TLT with ratios less than 1:4. Essentially, **Part I** includes the history, the theory, and the future of the TLT. The first two chapters of **Part I** present a review of 1:1 Baluns and 1:4 Baluns and Ununs (unbalanced to unbalanced transformers), as presented by Guanella and Ruthroff. Following that is my work on extending their approaches to TLTs with impedance ratios less than 1:4. **Chapter 4** contains information on TLTs with ratios greater than 1:4; in particular, 1:9, 1:12, and 1:16 are presented. Finally, important parameters, such as characteristic impedances for various types of conductors and efficiencies with various magnetic cores, are discussed, followed by a look at mistakes in the literature and the future direction of the TLT.

As was mentioned in the **Preface**, **Part II** presents the practical side of the TLT. It is essentially an update of my book, *Building and Using Baluns and Ununs*. Those chapters offer complete specifications and numerous photos of most of the devices.

Table of Contents

PART I—
UNDERSTANDING BALUNS AND UNUNS

Chapter 1

TLTs with 1:1 Ratios

The fundamental classification of the transmission line transformer (TLT) can be more easily categorized by impedance ratios than by Balun or Unun operation. This can be shown by the "basic building block" of Guanella in his classic 1944 paper[3] (see **Figure 1-1**), although he explained only the Balun operation when the center of the load, R_L, is grounded. In this case, Balun operation is assured

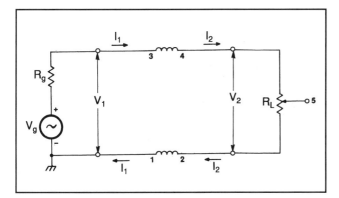

Figure 1-1. *The basic building block.*

when the inductive reactance of the top winding is at least 10 times greater than $R_L/2$. In other words, the reactance of the top winding should be five times greater than R_L at the lowest frequency of interest. When the characteristic impedance of the transmission line is equal to R_L, the upper frequency limit is mainly determined by self-resonance for coiled windings and the parasitics in the connections.

With toroidal cores, the inductive reactance at the lowest frequency of interest can be easily calculated. It simply involves the number of turns, N^2, divided by the effective length, which is the circumference of the center of the cross section of the torrid in turn divided by the permeability, times the cross section area. This relationship is then multiplied by a constant, which brings it to the proper unit, called a Henry. With rod cores, there is no simple equation for calculating the inductance—then one has to rely purely on experimentation.

There are two other important functions of the basic building block which were not described in

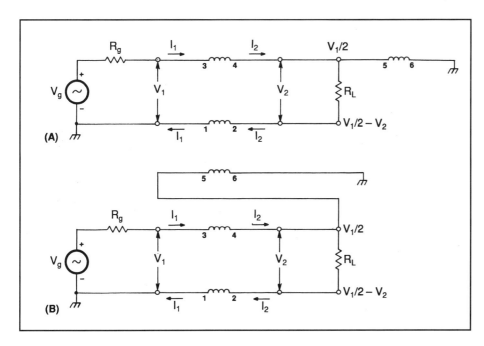

Figure 1-2. *(A) Ruthroff's 1:1 Balun high-frequency toroidal version model and (B) rod version.*

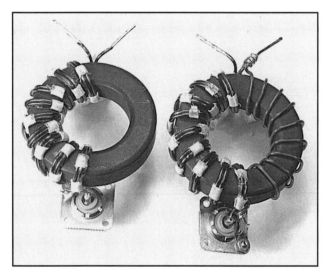

Photo 1-A. *Two basic forms of the 1:1 Balun.*

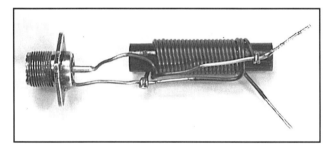

Photo 1-B. *A typical rod-type Balun.*

Guanella's classic paper. They are the phase inverter (when the top of R_L is grounded) and the delay line (when the bottom of R_L is grounded). In the delay line application, the voltage drop along the length of the transmission line is usually zero; therefore, there is no inductance and hence a core is required. Thus, Guanella's basic building block can be considered a 1:1 isolation transformer! In reviewing the Balun operation, the voltage drop is 1/2 V_1 and is $-V_1$ for the phase inverter. Because of the apparent isolation properties of the basic building block, it can also be used to change a Balun to an Unun, or vice versa. Since it has been shown that these transformers can exhibit such high efficiencies, especially when operat-

ing at low impedance levels, two or three TLTs can be connected in series to obtain the desired results.

Figure 1-2 shows two other versions of the 1:1 Balun which appeared after 1959. **Figure 1-2A** shows Ruthroff's model and **Figure 1-2B** shows a model by some unknown amateur using a rod core instead of a toroid. In Ruthroff's model, we see two inductances in series winding 3-4 and 5-6 forming a voltage divider resulting in terminal four being positive $V_1/2$ and terminal two being $V_1/2-V_2$. When R_L is grounded off its center, winding 5-6 becomes inoperative because of its very high reactance, resulting in a 1:1 Balun very much like Guanella's. But **Figure 1-2B** shows that winding 5-6 is always in the circuit and, not only does it reduce the characteristic impedance of windings 1-2 and 3-4, but it also couples the output impedance to the input impedance. In some cases, winding 5-6 is placed between the other two. With the trifilar nature of **Figure 1-2B**, the high-frequency response at the 50-ohm level can vary greatly at the high end. A suggested design would be simply the bifilar winding of 1-2 and 3-4 separated from its neighboring turns by about the diameter of the wires used. In this way the low-frequency response would be the same, but the high-frequency response would be much improved at the 50-ohm level. In other words, it becomes Guanella's form of the 1:1 (current) Balun.

Photo 1-A shows two forms of the 1:1 Balun. On the left is Guanella's and on the right is Ruthroff's. **Photo 1-B** shows the radio amateur's version of Ruthroff's model. As can be seen, the three windings are tightly coupled, yielding the undesirable results. **Photo 1-C** shows probably the latest amateur radio version of the 1:1 Balun. It consists of about 12 inches of 50-ohm cable threaded by ferrite beads. In order to obtain adequate isolation at the low frequency of 1.8 MHz, permeabilities in excess of 2000 are required. Manganese-zinc ferrite beads are, therefore, generally used in this case. As will be shown in **Chapter 5**, these beads exhibit excessive loss. In fact, beads have been known to literally fracture in this application because of the excessive heat.

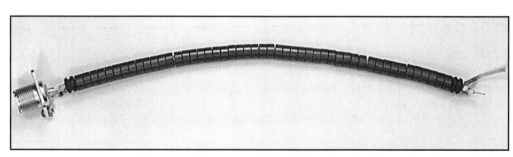

Photo 1-C. *The coaxial cable "choke" 1:1 Balun.*

Chapter 2

TLTs with 1:4 Ratios

The 1:4 TLT and the 1:1 TLT have been the most popular of the transmission line transformers. As Baluns, they have mostly been used in matching center-fed antennas to either coaxial cable or open wire transmission lines. The 1:4 Unun has mostly been used in broadband amplifiers.

The first version of the 1:4 TLT appeared in Guanella's classic 1944 paper[3]. **Figure 2-1** shows the high-frequency and low-frequency models of his Balun. In matching 50 ohms to 200 ohms, the transmission lines each see 1/2 of the load, R_L, and, therefore, the characteristic impedance of each transmission line should be 100 ohms. Since these two transmission lines are connected in parallel on the left side, the result is the desired value of 50 ohms. Since Guanella's TLTs sum voltages of equal delays, the high-frequency response is practically limited only by the parasitic in the connections. This assumes that the coiled transmission lines are not limiting the high-frequency response due to self-resonance.

The low-frequency model on the right in **Figure 2-1** shows that windings 3-4 and 5-6 are in series on the low-impedance side. If these windings are on separate cores their reactances are added in series. When operating at low-impedance levels, allowing for shorter transmission lines, the two transmission lines can be wound on a single toroid. This results in a gain of two times in the reactances in windings 3-4 and 5-6. In any event, the reactances of these two windings (or beaded lines) should be 10 times greater than the input impedance.

With reference to the basic building block discussed in **Chapter 1**, it should again be pointed out that Guanella's Balun can perform as a broadband delay line (Unun) when terminal 2 is grounded, and as a phase inverter when terminal 8 is grounded. It should be recognized that converting Guanella's 1:4 Balun to a 1:4 Unun yields exceptionally broadband widths and is an important design, especially for matching 50 ohms to 12.5 ohms.

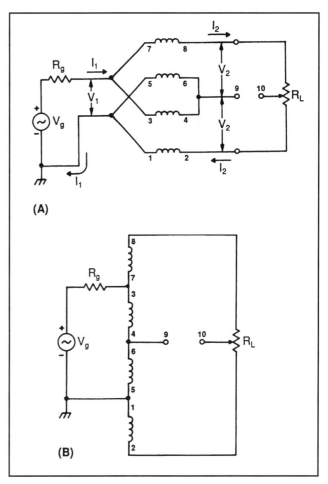

Figure 2-1. Electrical models of the Guanella 4:1 Balun: (A) high-frequency, (B) low-frequency.

In **Figure 2-2A** we see Ruthroff's high-frequency model for his 1:4 Unun and his 1:4 Balun in **Figure 2-2B**. In his 1:4 Unun he connects the high-voltage side of the input impedance to the end of the bottom transmission line. This lifts the whole transmission line by the voltage, V_1, resulting in a "bootstrap" effect. Since the transmission line sees 1/2 of the load, R_L, its characteristic impedance should also be 1/2. In the case of the Balun in **Figure 2-2B**, the

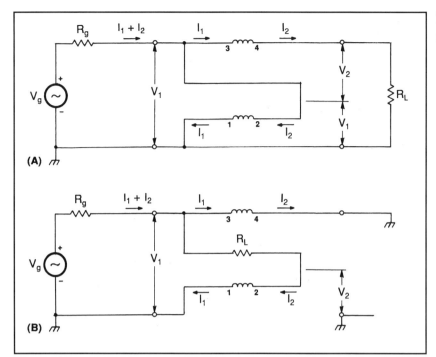

Figure 2-2. *The Ruthroff 1:4 transformers: (A) Unun and (B) Balun.*

basic building block is connected as a phase inverter. In this instance the characteristic impedance should also be 1/2 of the load, R_L, for maximum high-frequency response.

There are two major differences between Ruthroff's approach over that of Guanella's. It is somewhat simpler because it uses only one transmission line, but it also has a poorer high-frequency response since it adds a delayed voltage to a direct voltage. Thus, when the transmission line is a 1/2 wavelength long the output is zero. **Figure 2-3** shows the calculated losses of Ruthroff's 1:4 TLTs as a function of the transmission line length and characteristic impedance. As is shown when the transmission lines are 0.20 wavelength long, the loss is considerable. But for the radio amateur, usually operating below 30 MHz, 2/10 of a wavelength is equal to 2 meters in length, which is much longer than the lengths usually used in the TLTs.

Figure 2-4 shows the low-frequency models of Ruthroff's two TLTs. The model on the left is for his 1:4 Unun, which is identical to that of the autotransformer. The one on the right is for his 1:4 Balun.

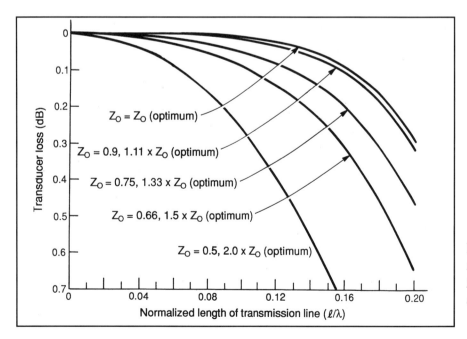

Figure 2-3. *Loss as a function of normalized transmission line length in a Ruthroff 1:4 Unun for various values of characteristic impedance, Z_O.*

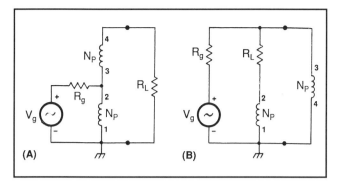

Figure 2-4. *Low-frequency models of the Ruthroff 1:4 transformers: (A) Unun and (B) Balun.*

Finally, **Photo 2-A** shows two versions of Guanella's 1:4 TLTs. The top TLT is a 1:4 Balun matching 50 ohms balanced to 12 1/2 ohms unbalanced. It uses tightly wound turns of No. 14 wire, yielding a characteristic impedance close to 25 ohms. The frequency response is flat from 1 1/2 MHz to about 50 MHz. The upper frequency response in this case is limited by the self-resonance of the windings. On the other hand, the bottom TLT shows a Guanella 1:4 Unun stepping down from 50 ohms unbalanced to 12 1/2 ohms unbalanced. It uses two 25-ohm coaxial cables, with one covered in ferrite beads. In this design, the response is flat from 10 MHz to well *over* 100 MHz!

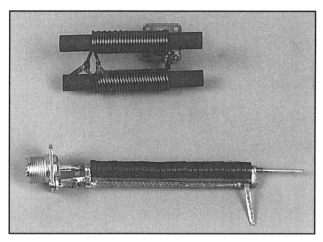

Photo 2-A. *Two Guanella 4:1 (50:12.5 ohm) Ununs: rod version (on the top), 1.5 to 50 MHz; beaded version (on the bottom), 10 MHz to over 100 MHz.*

The result of the two methods of obtaining 1:4 ratios can be categorized as follows: The Ruthroff bootstrap approach uses only one transmission line and can handle many applications when proper lengths of transmission lines are used. The Guanella approach always uses an added transmission line but, in turn, summons voltages of equal delays and, therefore, has a higher frequency response. The next chapter, which covers TLTs with ratios of less than 1:4, carries this same theme much further.

Chapter 3

TLTs with Ratios Less Than 1:4

The first two chapters of this book essentially gave the history of the TLT until about the middle of 1970. Some comments were made regarding publications in the amateur radio literature but they were not in anyway additions to the theory.

In working more with these broadband-matching devices, it became apparent that a need existed for impedance ratios greater than 1:1 and less than 1:4. If this was possible, important ratios like 1:1.33,

1:1.5, and 1:2 could result in important applications in antenna uses and logic circuits operating in the usual 50-ohm environment. These low ratios in series with other known TLTs result in important ratios never before obtained. These will be discussed in the next chapter.

My first attempt at obtaining a low-ratio TLT was in experimenting with the performance of a Ruthroff 1:4 Unun with a tap on its top winding. **Figure 3-1** shows the schematic. Two taps were employed: one at one turn from terminal 3 and the other at three turns. The experimental results are shown in **Figure 3-2**. There are seven total trifilar turns of No. 16 wire on a 4C4 toroid with an outside diameter of 1.5 inches and a permeability of 125. As is shown in the figure, the poorest performance occurs at the 24.5:50-ohm impedance level. The other two ratios exhibit wider bandwidth. Even though the bandwidths and efficiencies shown in **Figure 3-2** are quite poor, as will be shown later, they are still far superior to those of the autotransformer.

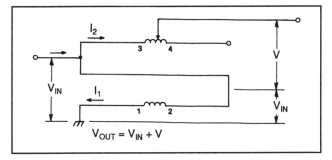

Figure 3-1. *Model for the analysis of the tapped bifilar transformer.*

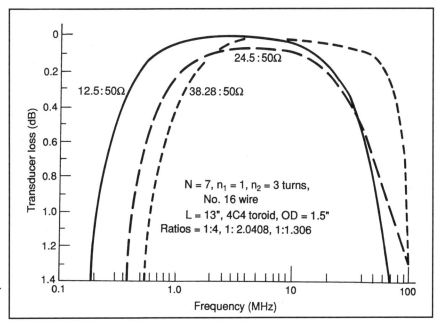

Figure 3-2. *Loss versus frequency for the tapped bifilar transformer.*

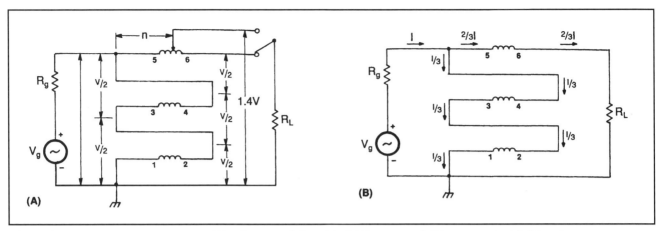

Figure 3-3. *Trifilar bootstrap Ununs: (A) voltages in 1:2 and 1: 2.25 ratios and (B) currents in 1:2.25 ratios.*

In order to improve upon the performance at around the 1:2 level, a trifilar connection that is an extension of Ruthroff's 1:4 "bootstrap technique" Unun is shown in **Figure 3-3**. **Figure 3-3A** shows the voltage relationships, including a tap on the top winding about 8/10 the distance from terminal 5 and yielding an output voltage very close to 1.4 times the input voltage, V. By connecting the load, R_L, directly to terminal 6, the output voltage is 1.5 times the input, yielding a natural ratio of 1: 2.25. This ratio should suffice in many 1:2 applications.

But the schematic in **Figure 3-3B** shows the currents that flow in this trifilar configuration. It is interesting to note that winding 5-6 in the 1:2.25 application carries 2/3 of the current, while the other two

windings carry 1/3 each. This means a transmission line mode occurs such that winding 5-6 is shared by windings 1-2 and 3-4. Another view is that two transmission lines operate in parallel with one winding common to both. Physically this means that this very efficient broadband TLT is basically comprised of two of Guanella's basic building blocks in parallel! From this model it becomes clear that the performance of this devise is based upon the fact that there is a direct voltage of V/2 from terminal 2 to ground and *two delayed voltages of V/2.*

The highly efficient and broadband performance of this trifilar Unun is shown in **Figures 3-4** and **3-5**. **Figure 3-4** shows the trifilar winding on a 1 1/2-inch toroid with a tap yielding a 1:2 ratio. As is shown in

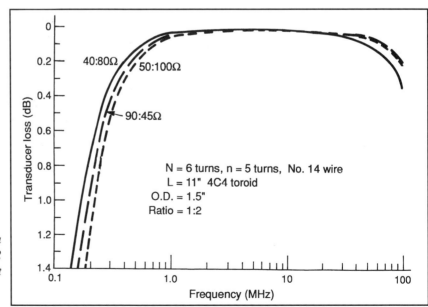

Figure 3-4. *Loss versus frequency for a tapped trifilar transformer at the 1:2 impedance ratio and at three different impedance levels.*

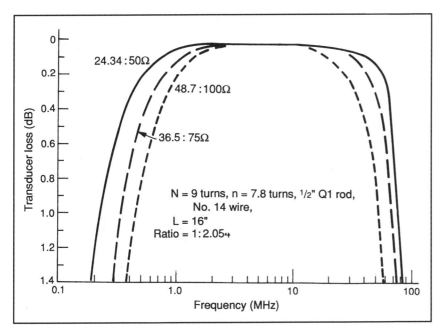

Figure 3-5. *Loss versus frequency for a tapped trifilar transformer using No. 14 wire on a 1/2-inch diameter Q1 rod and at three different impedance levels.*

the figure, the 50:100-ohm ratio is slightly better than the other two.

The efficiency and bandwidth shown here far exceed the 1:4 Ruthroff Unun since the voltage drops along the lengths of the windings are considerably less and the cancellation due to adding a direct voltage with the delayed one is considerably smaller. **Figure 3-5** shows the same trifilar winding on a 1 1/2-inch ferrite rod of similar permeability. Because the windings are tight to each other, the effective characteristic impedance concerning the top winding 5-6 is considerably lower. As is shown, the optimum performance occurs at the 24.34:50-ohm impedance level. This suggests that optimum performance at the 25:50-ohm impedance level for a toroidal core would probably occur if winding 5-6 in **Figure 3-3** were placed in between the other two. Examples are shown in **Part II** of this book.

Another revealing part of the story is illustrated in **Figure 3-6**, which shows two coaxial cables, connected in parallel and in Ruthroff bootstrap operation. The inner-conductor of the top coax is tapped at about 8/10 the distance from the left-hand edge, yielding a voltage ratio of 1.4 times the input voltage, V. **Figure 3-6A** shows the voltages and **Figure 3-6B** shows the currents at the 1:2.25 ratio. Since the voltage of each coax is 1/2 the input voltage, but the current in the top coax is twice that of the bottom one, its characteristic impedance should most likely be 1/2 that of the lower coax. For operations at the 25:50-ohm impedance level, the characteristic impedance of the top coax should be 25 ohms and that of the bottom 50 ohms. The application of coaxial cables looks very interesting.

Figure 3-7 shows a Guanella approach for a coiled wire TLT with ratios less than 1:4. Specifically, it shows a basic building block in parallel with a Guanella 1:4 Balun yielding a ratio of 2.25:1. The high-impedance side on the left shows the two TLTs in series and, on the right, the outputs in parallel. Since Guanella's TLTs are known to have equal delays for equal lengths of transmission lines, the high-frequency response is only limited by parasitics in the connections or self-resonance in coiled windings. In some instances, this form of TLT has been called an "equal-delay" TLT. If the impedance on the left is 100 ohms, the impedance on right side is 44.4 ohms. The optimum characteristic impedances of the transmission lines in this case are each 66 ohms. In matching 50 ohms to 22.22 ohms, the optimum characteristic impedances should be 33 ohms. For lower ratios, the bottom TLT in **Figure 3-7** should be changed to higher ratios. For example, with a 1:9 ratio the final overall ratio becomes 1.78:1, and for a 1:16 ratio in the bottom TLT the overall ratio becomes 1.56:1.

If the impedance on the left is 100 ohms, in the 1.78:1 ratio the ideal characteristic impedances should be 75 ohms for each transmission line; for the 1.56 ratio the characteristic impedances should be 80 ohms. When matching 50 ohms to lower impedances, the

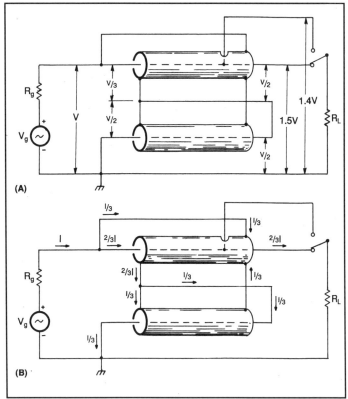

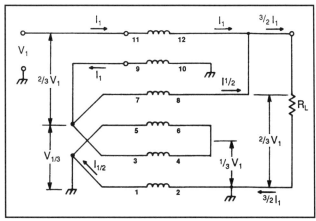

Figure 3-7. *High-frequency model of the parallel-type 2.25:1 transformer. Connections shown are for Unun operation.*

Figure 3-6. *Parallel coax Unun: (A) Voltages in 1:2 and 1:2.5 ratios and (B) currents in the 1:2.25 ratio.*

optimum characteristic impedances of the windings (or beaded coaxes) should be 37 1/2 and 40 ohms, respectively. Further descriptions of these equal-delay transformers are described in **Part II, Chapter 10** of this book and in Chapter 18 of my other TLT book.[1]

Figure 3-8 shows two quintufilar windings of a 1:1.56 Unun. The figure on the left is optimized for matching 50 to 75 ohms and that on the right to matching 50 to 33 ohms. Although not shown here, winding 9-10 carries 4/5 of the input current and the other windings carry 1/5 each. The other point to make in both the trifilar and quintufilar windings is that their low-frequency models show considerably more windings in series than their 1:4 counterpart. This means that fewer turns and, hence, shorter lengths can be employed in these higher order windings. Proof of this is shown in **Figure 3-9**, which illustrates the incredible performance at the 64:100-ohm impedance level using schematic "A" in **Figure 3-8**. As is shown, only three

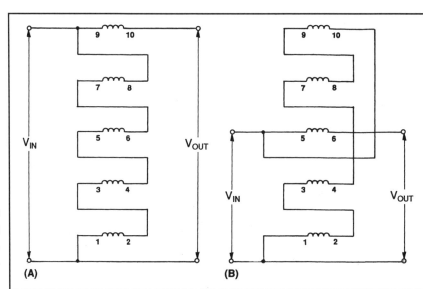

Figure 3-8. *Quintufilar transformers with impedance ratios of 1:1.56: (A) depicts a high-impedance operation and (B) displays windings configured for low-impedance operation.*

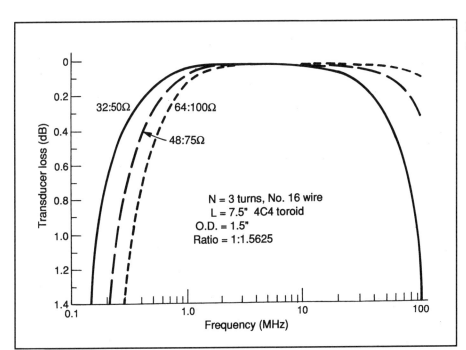

Figure 3-9. *Loss versus frequency for a five-winding transformer.*

turns of No. 16 wire is employed on the ferrite toroid with a permeability of 125. This performance even exceeds that of the trifilar one.

With shorter lengths of transmission line and higher permeabilities with smaller ferrite toroids, the bandwidths of these multi-conductor TLT's performances should be vastly improved. And, finally, tapping of the Guanella approach to these broadband low-ratio TLTs should be investigated. Since this technique is highly successful in the Ruthroff bootstrap approach, it is apparent that it should be also in the Guanella's equal-delay approach.

Chapter 4

TLTs with Ratios Greater Than 1:4

From TLTs with ratios less than 1:4, as described in **Chapter 3**, it is now possible to easily achieve Baluns and Ununs matching 50 ohms to impedances as high as 600 ohms and as low as 3.125 ohms. Since TLTs can be developed with very high efficiencies and broadband widths, several TLTs can be connected in series with their outstanding features.

This chapter begins with the two TLTs that resulted in high ratios using only one transformer. The first, shown in **Figure 4-1**, is the Guanella 1:9 Balun. **Figure 4-1A** is the high-frequency model and **Figure 4-1B** is the low-frequency model. The design objectives when matching 50 ohms to 450 ohms, the characteristic impedances, Z_O, of the three transmission lines should be 150 ohms. As can be seen, each transmission line sees 1/3 of the load, R_L. In **Figure 4-1B**, the reactance of winding 5-6 in series with winding 3-4, in turn, in parallel with windings 9-10 and 7-8 should be 10 times greater at the lowest frequency of interest—50 ohms. This transformer can operate even better in matching 5.5 ohms to 50 ohms. At lower impedance levels, lower reactances are required. Further, higher core permeabilities can be employed since core loss is impedance level dependent. This transformer can also operate as an Unun when terminal 2 is grounded. In this application, a 1:1 Balun on the output of a low-impedance Balun on the input of a high-impedance Balun (matching 50 ohms to 450 ohms) would help in the low-frequency response.

Figure 4-2 is a schematic of a trifilar-wound TLT using Ruthroff's bootstrap approach for obtaining a

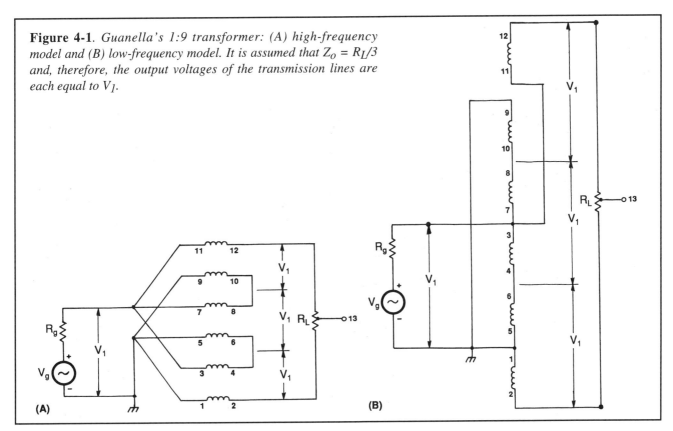

Figure 4-1. *Guanella's 1:9 transformer: (A) high-frequency model and (B) low-frequency model. It is assumed that $Z_O = R_L/3$ and, therefore, the output voltages of the transmission lines are each equal to V_1.*

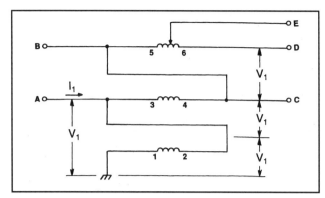

Figure 4-2. *A schematic diagram of a trifilar transformer for obtaining impedance ratios up to 1:9.*

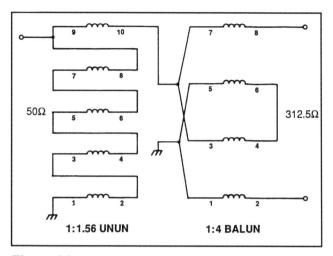

Figure 4-3. *Schematic diagram of the series-type Balun with a 1:6.25 ratio designed to match 50 to 312.5 ohms.*

variety of impedance-matching ratios from 1:2 up to 1:9. In the 1:9 ratio using terminals A-D, it shows a direct voltage added to a double delayed voltage. Therefore, the high-frequency response is much poorer than the other ratios. But at low-impedance levels, which require lower reactances and thus shorter lengths of transmission lines, this Unun makes a practical multi-match transformer for the HF band.

Figure 4-3 is a schematic for a 1:6.25 Balun matching 50 ohms to about 300 ohms. On the left is the extension of Ruthroff's technique to obtain an Unun with a ratio very close to 1:1.5, followed by a Guanella 1:4 Balun. By tapping the top winding in the Unun on the left, a ratio very close to 1:6 can be obtained. Further, by installing a 1:1 Balun in between these two TLTs and grounding terminal 2 in the 1:4 Balun, a broadband 1:6 Unun results.

Figure 4-4 is a schematic of a Balun matching 50 ohms to 600 ohms, yielding a ratio of 1:12. The Unun on the left is a tapped quintufilar winding, yielding a ratio of 1:1.33 in series with a 1:9 Guanella Balun. A septufilar-wound Unun can also be used. By installing a 1:1 basic building block in between these two TLTs and grounding terminal 2 of the 1:9 Balun, a broadband 1:12 Unun results.

Broadband ratios of 1:16 can also be obtained with the Guanella approach. It would contain four transmission lines in a parallel series connection. For the Ruthroff approach, it would be two 1:4 Ununs in series. With appropriate characteristic impedances, broadband operation is possible at these very high ratios.

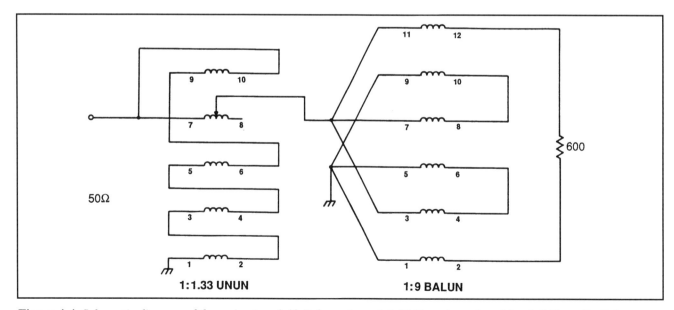

Figure 4-4. *Schematic diagram of the series-type 1:12 Balun using a 1:1.33 Unun in series with a 1:9 Guanella Balun.*

Chapter 5

Characterization

The word characterization is very familiar to those engaged in the research and development of Solid-State devices. It involves the study of the various components that make up the models of the particular devises. In the case of TLTs, we have two models of each transformer as previously mentioned: one is the high-frequency model and the other the low-frequency model. The major subject of interest with the high-frequency model is the characteristic impedance, Z_O, of the transmission lines employed. Having many types of transmission lines available leads to the major investigation to develop the proper values of characteristic impedance. It is assumed that the proper model has been chosen, whether it's Guanella's with its equal delays, or Ruthroff's with his bootstrap application. The make-up of the magnetic cores, which are usually ferrites, is also a study of interest. For high-power applications, the bulk resistivity becomes an important ingredient. In the low-frequency model, the reactance of the coiled or beaded transmission line at the lowest frequency of interest is the important consideration. Here, number of turns, permeability of the cores, and geometry of the cores all come into play.

Since this topic covers so much territory, only a few of the major subjects can be included in this chapter. The first topic deals with the geometry of the cores and the permeability of the material. **Figure 5-1** shows three TLTs with the same windings but with different cores. Two are toroids and one is a rod. One is a powered-iron toroid with a permeability of only 10. The other two use Q1 ferrite material with permeabilities of 125. As is shown, the powered-iron core with a permeability of 10 has the poorest low-frequency response, and the ferrite toroid with a permeability of 125 has the best low-frequency response of the three. Also clearly shown is the poorer response of a rod core of four inches in length compared to its counterpart, the toroidal core. Further, there is no simple formula for calculating the so-called "magnetizing

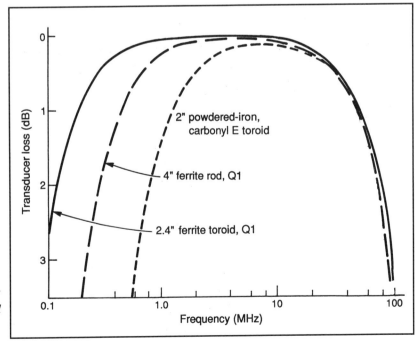

Figure 5-1. *Experimental results showing the low-frequency performance of the rod transformer versus the toroidal transformer.*

MATERIAL	SUPPLIER	PERMEABILITY	BULK RESISTIVITY (ohms-cm)
Q1 (NiZn)	Allen Bradley (formerly Indiana General)	125	10^8
G (NiZn)	Allen Bradley	300	10^6
Q2 (NiZn)	Allen Bradley	40	10^9
H (NiZn)	Allen Bradley	850	10^4 - 10^5
4C4 (NiZn)	Ferroxcube	125	10^7 - 10^8
3C8 (MnZn)	Ferroxcube	2700	10^2 - 10^3
K5 (NiZn)	MH&W Intl (TDK)	290	2×10^6
KR6 (NiZn)	MH&W Intl (TDK)	2000	10^5 - 10^6
CMD5005 (NiZn)	Ceramic Magnetics	1400	7×10^9
C2025 (NiZn)	Ceramic Magnetics	175	5×10^6
CN20 (NiZn)	Ceramic Magnetics	800	10^6
C2050 (NiZn)	Ceramic Magnetics	100	3×10^7
E (Powdered Iron)	Arnold Engineering, Amidon Associates	10	10 -2

Table 5-1. *Cores, suppliers, and specifications.*

inductance" when using a rod. The low-frequency results for this core are mainly determined experimentally. Rod cores have found favor in the past for amateur radio use because they are generally less expensive than their toroidal counterparts.

Table 5-1 shows a listing of the various core materials used in my investigation. Since this goes back to about 1975, it is expected that some of the manufacturers are no longer in existence and that new sources are available. A particular example is the K5 material,

which is shown in succeeding figures. Since this material was manufactured in Japan, it has now been excluded because any compound using nickel is now considered a serious contaminant. Other countries still manufacture ferrites of nickel-zinc, however.

The two parameters that are important in TLTs are having ferrite materials that are both high in permeability and bulk resistivity. The importance of the latter parameter can be shown in the next two figures. **Figure 5-2** shows the response curve of two TLTs

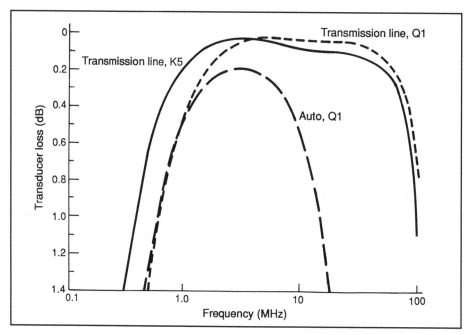

Figure 5-2. *Performance of 4:1 transformers operating at the 100:25-ohm level.*

Figure 5-3. *Loss versus frequency of four 4:1 transformers at the 200:50-ohm level.*

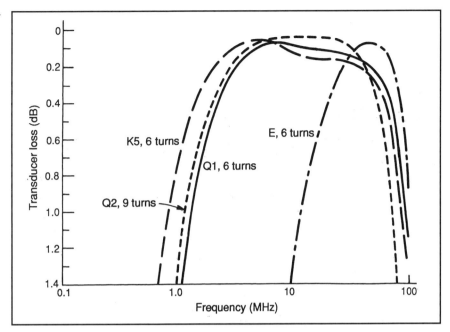

using different permeabilities and compared to an autotransformer with the material (Q1) of one of the TLTs. As can be seen when matching at the 100:25-ohm level, the K5 material has a better low-frequency response but a little more loss above 10 MHz.

Figure 5-3 shows the comparisons at the higher impedance level of 200:50 ohms. The difference between K5 and Q1 becomes larger at the higher impedance level. Also shown in the figure are the results of Q2 with a permeability of 40 and E with a permeability of only 10.

Figure 5-4 clearly shows the expected performance with lower bulk resistivities. The 3C8 ferrite has a permeability of 2700 and a bulk resistivity of only 10^2–10^3. The other two curves are from KR6 with a permeability of 2000 and a bulk resistivity of 10^5–10^6, and H at a permeability of 850 and 10^4–10^5.

Experiments with various materials show the importance of investigating the losses of the materials, particularly as a function of impedance level. The 3C8 material has been used on the so-called "choke" Balun, a beaded 50-ohm coaxial cable, which explains why the

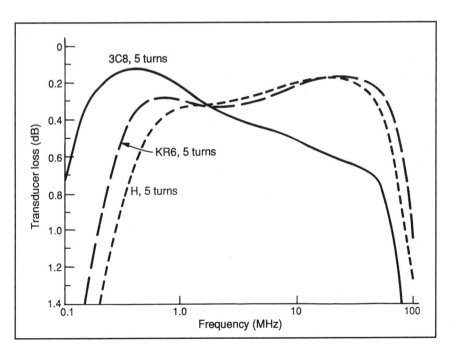

Figure 5-4. *Measurements of 3C8, KR6, and H materials at the 200:50-ohm level.*

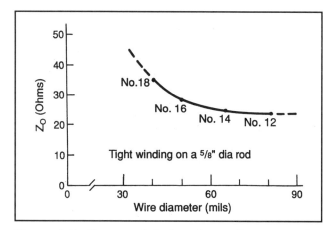

Figure 5-5. *Characteristic impedance, Z_O, versus wire diameter for a tightly wound transformer (tight winding on a 5/8-inch diameter rod).*

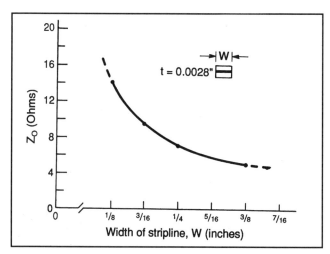

Figure 5-6. *Measured values of the characteristic impedance, Z_O, of striplines versus width.*

beads have been known to fracture due to excessive heat. By the use of ferrites with a permeability of 125 and very much larger cores for added dissipation, TLTs with 50:200-ohm ratios have been known to operate satisfactorily at the 10–20-kilowatt level.[5]

In the investigation of various transmission lines, two interesting results can be shown. **Figure 5-5** shows the variation of characteristic impedance for tightly wound transmission lines on a ferrite rod. The figure shows that No. 14 wire has a characteristic impedance of about 25 ohms in a tightly wound configuration. By separating the bifilar windings by about one wire diameter or winding it around a toroid, the characteristic impedance approaches 50 ohms. When

working at impedance levels of 200:300 ohms, characteristic impedances of 100:150 ohms require extra spacing using Teflon™ sleeving and, generally, toroids are used instead of rods.

Figure 5-6 shows the experimental results of a stripline transmission line. As shown, characteristic impedances approaching 5 ohms are obtainable! With thinner insulation, low impedances can be obtained with less widths.

Figure 5-7 shows the results of two Ruthroff TLTs in series using stripline matching 50 ohms to about 3 ohms. By using two Guanella 1:4 Ununs, each using a transmission line as a delay line, bandwidths greatly exceeding those shown in **Figure 5-7** are expected.

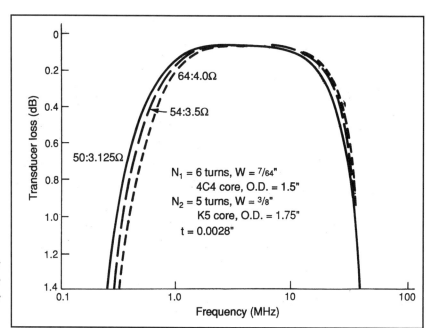

Figure 5-7. *Experimental results of the 16:1 transformer of Figure 4-4 at three different impedance levels. Note the best level is at about 54:3.5 ohms.*

Chapter 6

Summary

After many talks before amateur and professional groups, as well as during a recent literature search on diode mixers and power splitter/combiners, it became apparent that very few really understood transmission line transformer technology. Prime examples of this misunderstanding follow.

Figure 6-1 shows a schematic diagram of a diode mixer. The author states that the transformer, T-1, is a TLT. He assumes it is a TLT because its windings are twisted. But from the schematic it can be easily shown that T-1 has a primary and secondary winding like any conventional transformer in which it transmits the energy from input to output by flux linkages. The idea of twisting came from Ruthroff's approach. He worked with very small toroids and fine wires. In order to keep the characteristic impedance of the transmission lines under control he had to twist the wires.

Another author also employed a twisting of wires. **Figure 6-2** shows the transformer, which he called a TLT, used in his schematic. The input current, 2I, splits into two currents, which flow out of the two secondary terminals. The voltages of the three terminals are the same. Since it can be seen that the currents through the transformer are equal and opposite, there is virtually no voltage drop between its terminals because of flux canceling. Furthermore, since the input on the right side has an impedance half that of the two outputs, a 1:2 transformer is required to bring the circuit back to 50 ohms. The 1:2 transformer used in the author's schematic is an autotransformer, as was shown in **Chapter 5**, it is vastly inferior in bandwidth and efficiency to a TLT. And, finally, the theory of the flux-canceling transformer is certainly not that of a TLT and requires further study.

In reviewing the history of the TLT, we've seen that two approaches had been used until about 1970.

The first was Guanella's, which for 1:4, 1:9, and 1:16 TLTs used transmission lines connected in parallel at the low-impedance side and in series at the high-

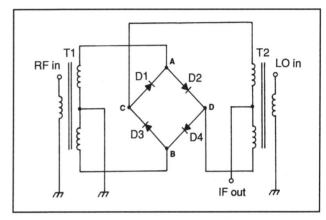

Figure 6-1. *Equivalent circuit of a double-balanced mixer using four diodes in a ring configuration.*

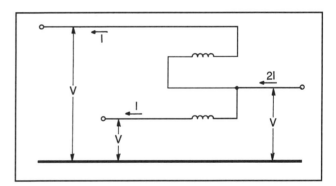

Figure 6-2. *Typical power combiner/splitter circuit.*

impedance side. Essentially he summed voltages of equal delays. Therefore, his TLTs, which were essentially Baluns, had high-frequency responses only limited by the parasitics. His 1:1 basic building block and 1:4 Balun are the Baluns of choice today.

Ruthroff, on the other hand, used Guanella's basic building block for obtaining a 1:4 ratio by connecting the basic building block in a bootstrap configuration. He was able to produce a broadband 1:4 Unun. By connecting the basic building block in a phase-inverter configuration he was able to obtain a broadband 1:4 Balun. But his 1:4 TLTs summed a direct voltage with a delayed voltage, which eventually ended up in a canceling mode, thereby limiting the high-frequency response. For many applications not requiring vary large bandwidths, his simple TLTs are applicable.

After 1970 advances where made, particularly with the 1:4, 1:2, and 1:1.5 Unun. The improved 1:4 Unun used Guanella's equal-delay approach by employing one of the basic building blocks as a delay line. Since this transmission line has no voltage drop across it, no magnetic medium is required. The other transmission line has the same voltage drop across it as the Ruthroff Unun, thus resulting in the same low-frequency response.

As was shown in **Chapter 3**, by using a trifilar bootstrap approach, improved bandwidth at the 1:2.25 ratio results. By tapping one of the conductors, a ratio of practically 1:2 can be obtained. By using five conductors in a quintufilar arrangement, broadband ratios of 1:1.5 are easily obtained. Since the delayed voltage is four times the direct voltage, this TLT has even much broader bandwidth than the 1:4 and 1:2 ratios. These ratios, again as shown in **Chapter 3**, can also be obtained by using Guanella's equal-delay approach. A 1:1 basic building block in series/parallel with a 1:4 Guanella TLT results in a very broadband 1:2.25 ratio. This is also called an equal-delay TLT. By using the basic building block in series parallel with Guanella's 1:16 TLT, a broadband equal-delay 1:1.56 ratio results. Although, to the best of my knowledge it has not been tried, tapping one conductor in the basic building block, which is connected in series parallel with the 1:4 equal-delay TLT, could result in a ratio close to 1:2. The choice one makes at the 1:1.5 ratio is still not clear.

The bootstrap approach has the advantage of using only one magnetic medium with all the conductors in a series aiding operation, which could make this device very practical in many applications. Undoubtedly, the equal-delay method suffers at the low-frequency end and requires *five* transmission lines, reducing its application. It is clear that the 1:4 and 1:2.25 equal-delay TLTs have much wider bandwidths than their counterparts.

When viewing the results of the various experiments performed on the TLT, it becomes apparent that this technology is not suited for the vacuum tube with its high impedances, but for the Solid-State devices of today with their lower impedances. With the application of the equal-delay approaches of Guanella and the low-impedance ratios of Ruthroff's bootstrap approach, the future is bright for the application of these broadband TLTs at low-impedance levels. With modern fabrication techniques, the TLT, in matching 50 ohms down to lower impedances, should have a capability greatly exceeding 100 MHz!

And, finally, for those interested in writing a comprehensive text like that of the renowned Frederick E. Terman,[6] I suggest including the simplified and unified approach to the theory of the very broadband, impedance-matching TLT shown in this book.

In closing, I feel it necessary to include a small tutorial on grammar. The "Balun" which is well known, is a match between a balanced impedance and an unbalanced impedance. The "Unun," a word I coined several years ago, came about because there was no acceptable term for a device matching unbalanced impedance to unbalanced impedance, and it became quite tedious to continuously type the whole expression. In discussing this device on the air, I found many called it a U-nun—obviously the right terminology is Un-un.

References

1. Jerry Sevick, *Transmission Line Transformers*, 4th edition, Noble Publishing Corporation, 2001.

2. Jerry Sevick, *Building and Using Baluns and Ununs*, 1st edition, CQ Communications Inc., 1994.

3. G. Guanella, "Novel Matching Systems for High Frequencies," *Brown-Boveri Review*, Volume 31, September 1944, pages 327–329.

4. C.L. Ruthroff, "Some Broad-Band Transformers," *Proceedings of the IRE*, Volume 47, August 1959, pages 1337–1342.

5. J. Terleski, <arraysolutions.com> website.

6. F.E. Terman, *Electronic and Radio Engineering*, 4th edition, McGraw-Hill Book Co., 1955

PART II—
BUILDING AND USING
BALUNS AND UNUNS

Chapter 7

The 1:1 Balun

Sec 7.1   Introduction

In this chapter I will introduce the most popular broadband Balun in amateur radio use—the 1:1 Balun. This topic been discussed in the amateur radio literature since the publication of Turrin's 1964 article.[8] Although Turrin's Balun is really a version of Ruthroff's, which was introduced in his classic 1959 article,[9] the real beginning of the broadband 1:1 Balun dates back to Guanella's classic paper of 1944.[3] Guanella's objective was to design a broadband 16:1 Balun to match the balanced output impedance of 960 ohms of a push-pull, 100-watt vacuum-tube amplifier to the unbalanced load of a matched 60-ohm coaxial cable. Use of his approach for 1:1, 4:1, and 9:1 Baluns has produced the designs of choice. They are presently called current or choke Baluns.

This chapter begins with an introduction to the technology of transmission line transformers. Other topics discussed include: 1) when to use a Balun; 2) highlights of significant articles in the professional and amateur radio literature; 3) high-power, medium-power, and low-power designs; and 4) isolation transformers. The latter is presented here for the first time. The chapter closes with a brief summary of the significant points included within.

Sec 7.2   When to Use a Balun

Baluns have taken on a more significant role in the past few decades with the advent of solid-state transceivers and Class B linear amplifiers with unbalanced outputs. That is, the voltage on the center conductor of their output chassis connectors varies (plus and minus) with respect to ground. In many cases, coaxial cables are used as the transmission lines from these unbalanced outputs to antennas like dipoles, inverted Vs, and Yagi beams that favor a balanced feed. In essence, they prefer a source of power whose terminals are balanced (voltages being equal and opposite) with respect to actual ground or to the virtual ground

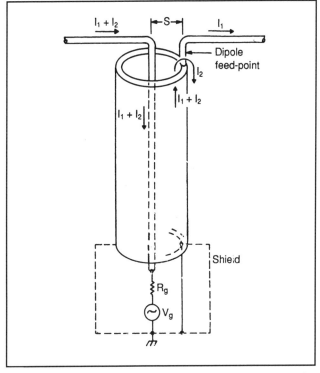

Figure 7-1. *An illustration of the various currents at the feedpoint of a dipole. I_1 is the dipole current and I_2, the inverted L (imbalance) current.*

that bisects the center of the antenna. The question that is asked most frequently is whether a 1:1 Balun is really needed.

To illustrate the problem involved and to give a basis for my suggestions, I refer you to **Figure 7-1**. Here we have, at the feedpoint of the dipole, two equal and opposite transmission line currents with two components each—I_1 and I_2. Also shown is the spacing, s, between the center conductor and the outside braid. Theoretically, a balanced antenna with a balanced feed would have a ground (zero potential) plane bisecting this spacing. However, because a coax-feed is unbalanced and the outer braid is also connected to ground at some point, an imbalance exists at the feed-point giving rise to two antenna modes. One lies with I_1, providing a dipole mode; the other lies with I_2, providing an inverted L mode.

If the spacing, s, is increased, the imbalance at the feedpoint becomes greater—giving rise to more current on the outer braid and a larger imbalance of currents on the antenna's arms. Several steps can be taken to eliminate or minimize the undesirable inverted L mode (that is, eliminate or minimize I_2). The obvious choice is to use a well-designed Balun that not only provides a balanced feed, but also minimizes (by its choking reactance) I_2—if the coaxial cable does not lie in the ground plane that bisects the center of the dipole. The other step is to ground the coaxial cable at a quarter-wave (or odd-multiple thereof) from the feedpoint. This discourages the inverted L mode because any radiating element will want to see a high impedance at these lengths instead of the low imped-ance of a ground connection.

I conducted experiments with Baluns on a 20-meter half-wave dipole at a height of 0.17 wavelengths, which gave a resonant impedance of 50 ohms. VSWR curves were compared under various conditions. When the coaxial cable was in the ground plane of the antenna (that is, perpendicular to the axis of the anten-na), the VSWR curves were identical with or without a well-designed Balun—no matter where the outer braid was grounded. A significant difference was noted only when the coaxial cable was out of the ground plane. When the cable dropped down at a 45-degree angle under the dipole, a large change in the VSWR took place. This meant that the inverted L mode was appreciable.

It should also be mentioned that the direction of I_2, the imbalance current, can depend upon the side on which the coaxial cable is out of the ground plane of the dipole. For example, if the cable comes down under the right side in **Figure 7-1** (that is, the angle between the horizontal arm and the coax is less than 90 degrees on the right side and more than 90 degrees on the left side), then the direction of I_2 can be reversed by the imbalance in the induced currents on the outside of the braid. By the same token, by having the coaxial cable coming down on the other side, the value of I_2 is only increased in magnitude.

However, feeding a Yagi beam without a well-designed 1:1 Balun is a different matter. Because most Yagi designs use shunt-feeding (usually by hairpin matching networks) in order to raise the input imped-

ance close to 50 ohms, the effective spacing (s) is greatly increased. Furthermore, the center of the dri-ven element is actually grounded. Thus, connecting the outer braid (which is grounded at some point) to one of the input terminals, creates a large imbalance and a real need for a Balun. An interesting solution, which would eliminate the matching network, is to use a step-down Balun designed to match 50-ohm cable directly to the lower balanced-impedance of the driven element.[2]

In summary, if you concur with the theoretical model of **Figure 7-1**, my experiments performed on 20 meters, and the reports from radio amateurs using dipoles and inverted Vs without Baluns, then it appears that 1:1 Baluns are really needed for: a) Yagi beam antennas where severe pattern distortion can take place without one, and b) dipoles and inverted Vs that have the coaxial cable feed lines out of the ground plane that bisects the antennas, or that are unbalanced by their proximity to manmade or natural structures. In general, the need for a Balun is not so critical with dipoles and inverted Vs (especially on 40, 80, and 160 meters) because the diameter of the coax-ial cable connector at the feedpoint is much smaller than the wavelength.

If my model, which assumes that a part of the prob-lem when feeding balanced antennas with coaxial cable is related to the size of the spacing, s (shown in **Figure 7-1**), then the possibility exists for using Ununs for matching into balanced antennas with impedances other than 50 ohms and with small values of s. For example, half-wave dipoles at a height of about a half-wave, quads, and center-fed 3/2-wave dipoles—which all have impedances close to 100 ohms—could very well be matched to 50-ohm cable by a 2:1 Unun. As I will show, they are considerably easier to construct than 2:1 Baluns. Furthermore, Genaille[10] has recently shown considerable success using Ununs in this kind of application.

To wind up this section, I would like to comment on an article published by Eggers,[11] WA9NEW, concern-ing the use of a Balun with a half-wave dipole. While at North Carolina State University, he conducted an experimental investigation of pattern distortion with-out a Balun at 1.6 GHz in an RF anechoic chamber (which simulates "free space"). Briefly, his results showed that, with a Balun (bazooka type), the antenna radiation pattern compared very favorably with the classic "figure-eight." Without the Balun, the radiation pattern was severely distorted.

Even though the author expressed difficulty in obtaining accurate measurements at this very high frequency, I have a question regarding the validity of performing the experiment in the first place. From the photograph in the article, it appears that conventional coaxial cable and connectors were used in the experiment. If we assume an effective diameter of 0.375 inches for these components, then scaling up to 3.5 MHz (457.14 fold) results in a coaxial cable with a diameter of 14.28 feet! I am quite sure that the large spacing, s, of 7.14 feet would bring about a noticeable imbalance resulting in appreciable pattern distortion even at 3.5 MHz.

Sec 7.3   Highlights of Significant Articles on 1:1 Baluns

Although there have been many articles on 1:1 Baluns published in the professional and amateur literature, I have selected for review a few that I believe have had the most impact on 1:1 Baluns for amateur radio use. As you will see, even though I consider some of the amateur articles significant, their impact upon the use and understanding of these devices has not always been positive. In fact, in some cases, the opposite has been true.

In the professional literature

There are actually only two significant articles in the professional literature that provide the fundamental principles upon which the theory and design of this class of transformers are based. It can be said that succeeding investigators simply extended the works of the authors of these two articles.

The first presentation on broadband matching transformers using transmission lines was given by Guanella in 1944.[3] He coiled transmission lines forming a choke such that only transmission line currents were allowed to flow, no matter where a ground was connected to the load. His single, coiled transmission line resulted in a 1:1 Balun. It is shown schematically in **Figure 7-2A**. Prior to this, RF Baluns were achieved by the use of quarter and half-wave transmission lines, and as a result, had narrow bandwidths. Guanella then demonstrated broadband Baluns with impedance transformations of $1:n^2$ where n is the number of transmission lines he connected in a series-parallel arrangement.

Several important points should be made regarding Guanella's 1:1 Balun shown in **Figure 7-2A**. With

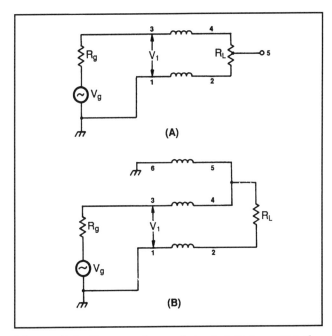

Figure 7-2. *Two versions of the 1:1 Balun: (A) the Guanella Balun and the basic building block; (B) the Ruthroff Balun as originally drawn.*

sufficient choking reactance, the output is isolated from the input and only flux-canceling transmission line currents are allowed to flow. With matched or very short transmission lines, the grounding of terminal 5 (actually or virtually like the center of a dipole) results in terminal 4 becoming $+V_1/2$ and terminal 2 becoming $-V_1/2$—creating a balanced output. This type of Balun has lately been called a "current" or "choke" Balun. A significant feature of this model is that a potential gradient of $-V_1/2$ exists along the length of the transmission line. This gradient, which exists on both conductors, accounts for practically all of the loss in these transformers because the loss mechanism is voltage dependent (a dielectric-type loss). All transmission line transformers have some sort of voltage gradient along their transmission lines and are, thus, subject to the same type of losses. Furthermore, the theory and loss mechanism is the same whether the transmission lines are coax or twin-lead, or coiled around cores, or threaded through ferrite beads. Additionally, it was shown[2] that higher-impedance Baluns or Baluns subjected to higher VSWRs have more loss because the voltage gradients are also larger.

The second significant article on broadband transmission line transformers was published by Ruthroff.[9] His 1:1 Balun, which is shown as originally drawn in

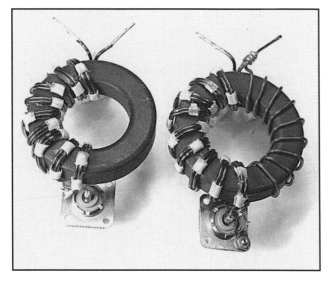

Photo 7-A. *The two basic forms of the 1:1 Balun that first appeared in the professional literature. The two-conductor Guanella Balun is on the left and the three-conductor Ruthroff Balun is on the right.*

Figure 7-2B, used an extra winding to complete (as he said) the path for the magnetizing current. Even though his schematic drawing appeared to look like a trifilar winding, his pictorial in the article clearly showed that the third winding (5-6) was on a separate part of the toroid. With an equal number of turns, it forms a voltage divider with winding (3-4) placing terminal 4 at $+V_1/2$ and terminal 2 at $-V_1/2$. In his classic paper, Ruthroff also presented his form of the 4:1 Balun (which is also different from Guanella's), a 4:1 Unun, and various hybrids. **Photo 7-A** shows the two basic forms of the 1:1 Balun that first appeared in the professional literature. The two-conductor Guanella 1:1 Balun is on the left and the three-conductor Ruthroff Balun is on the right. As was mentioned before, the Guanella Balun has also been called a "current" or "choke" Balun.

Before moving on to the significant articles in the amateur radio literature, some mention should be made of the differences between the two basic forms shown in **Photo 7-A**. Guanella's 1:1 Balun came to be known as the *basic building block* for this whole class of broadband transformers. This term was coined by Ruthroff as he showed its 1:1 Balun capability when the load was grounded at its center (terminal 5), and as a phase-inverter when the load was grounded at the top (terminal 4). By connecting terminal 2 to terminal 3 and connecting the bottom of the load to ground, Ruthroff demonstrated his very popular 4:1 Unun. I

call this type of arrangement the bootstrap connection. By grounding terminal 2, there is no potential drop along the transmission line and, therefore, no need for magnetic cores or beads. This arrangement, which turns out to be an important function for extending the high frequency performance of this class of transformers, I call the "phase-delay" connection.

Thus, with the flexibility shown by Guanella's basic building block, a 1:1 Balun is now realized that not only presents a balanced power source to a balanced antenna system, but can also prevent an imbalance current (an inverted L antenna current) by its choking reactance when the load is unbalanced or mismatched or when the feedline is not perpendicular to the axis of the antenna.

Interestingly enough, except at the very low end of the frequency response of the Ruthroff 1:1 Balun where autotransformer action can take place, his Balun takes on the characteristics of the Guanella Balun. The reactance of the third winding becomes great enough to make it literally transparent. This is not the nature of the trifilar-wound (voltage) Balun, which is sensitive to unbalanced and mismatched loads over its entire passband because it is actually two tightly coupled transmission lines. This distinction was not recognized by most of those who published in the amateur radio literature.

In the amateur radio literature

R. Turrin, W2IMU—1964

The first presentation in the amateur radio literature on 1:1 Baluns using ferrite cores was by Turrin in 1964.[8] Turrin, who was a colleague of Ruthroff's at Bell Labs, took his small-signal design (which used No. 37 or 38 wire on toroids with ODs of 0.25 inches or less) and adapted it to high-power use. This was done by using thicker wire, larger cores, and (very importantly for high efficiency[2]) low permeability ferrite. Ruthroff used lossy manganese-zinc ferrites with permeabilities of about 3000 because efficiency was not a major consideration.

Figure 7-3 is a pictorial and a schematic of Turrin's design. As you can see, the third wire (winding 3-4) is placed between the two current-carrying wires (windings 1-2 and 4-5). **Photo 7-B** shows (on the left) his actual design using a ferrite core; a popular design (on the right) using a powdered-iron core is available in kit form from Amidon Associates, Inc. Both Baluns use 10 trifilar turns of a single-coated wire like Formex™ or Formvar™ on a toroid. Turrin's design

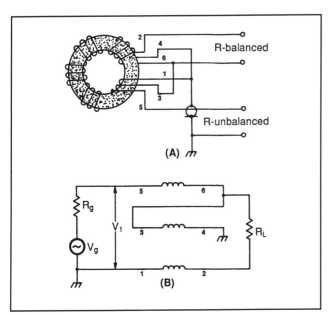

Figure 7-3. *(A) A pictorial of Turrin's 1:1 Balun, and (B) a schematic of his Balun.*

uses a ferrite toroid with an OD of 2.4 inches and a permeability of 40. The Amidon Associates' Balun uses a powdered-iron toroid with a 2-inch OD and a permeability of only 10. Both Baluns are specified to handle 1000 watts of power from 1.8 to 30 MHz.

Figure 7-4 shows the response curves for these two Baluns when terminated with 50-ohm loads. The response curve for a popular 1:1 rod-type Balun that uses the same schematic and wire is also shown. It has 8 trifilar turns, tightly wound on a rod of 0.5-inch diameter, 2.5 inches long, and with a permeability of 125. The rod-type Balun is shown in **Photo 7-C**.

Several important features should be brought out regarding the results shown in **Figure 7-4**. They are:

1. All Baluns had insufficient choking reactance and, hence, poor low-frequency responses. The powdered-iron version was especially poor. They all showed a drop in the input impedance and an inductive component at 2 MHz. This meant flux in the cores and an undesirable condition—especially for ferrite, which is a nonlinear material. Ferrite cores could not only suffer damage, but they could also generate spurious frequencies under these conditions. In fact, the same condition could occur at 4 MHz with a VSWR of 2:1! Therefore, I don't recommend any of these Baluns for use on 160 or 80 meters.

2. The major problem at the low-frequency end is the role of the third winding (3-4) in **Figure 7-3B**. It has been claimed[12] that the third winding improves the low-frequency response (over the two-conductor Guanella 1:1 Balun) because it enables autotransformer action at the low end. However, recent measurements I have made on two-conductor Guanella Baluns and three-conductor Ruthroff (or Turrin) Baluns, with loads grounded at their centers, show insignificant differences. This type of load approximates the actual condition when feeding a balanced antenna system. The negative feature of the third winding (3-4) is that, at the low-frequency end, there can be insufficient reactance to prevent harmful flux in the core because of a direct shunting path to ground. With the two-conductor 1:1 Balun, the only flux-inducing current is that of the imbalance current (the inverted L mode), which is usually far smaller.

3. Another important feature of the curves shown in **Figure 7-4** is the effect of the characteristic impedances of the coiled transmission lines. For example, a bifilar winding (wires tight together) on a toroid with spacing between adjacent bifilar turns exhibits a char-

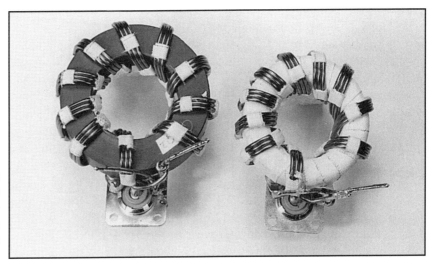

Photo 7-B. *Two versions of Turrin's design: On the left, the 1:1 Balun that has appeared in the amateur radio literature; on the right, a 1:1 Balun that has been readily available in kit form from Amidon Associates, Inc.*

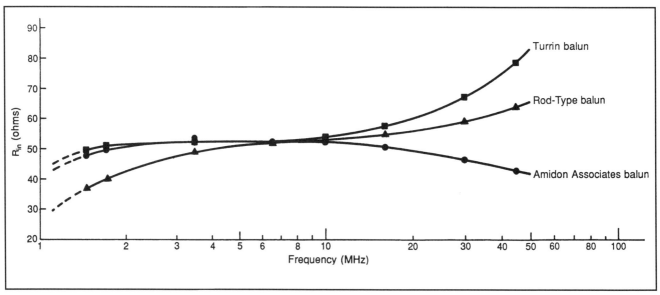

Figure 7-4. *The input impedance versus frequency, when terminated with 50 ohms, for the Turrin, typical rod-type, and Amidon Associates 1:1 Baluns.*

acteristic impedance of about 45 ohms. When wound on a rod with no space between adjacent bifilar turns, the characteristic impedance drops to about 25 ohms. With the third winding (3-4) between the other two as shown in **Figure 7-3B**, the characteristic impedance is raised to approximately 70 ohms in the toroidal case and to about 47 ohms in the rod case. If the toroidal Baluns were terminated in 70 ohms and the rod Balun terminated in 47 ohms, the high-frequency responses would be practically flat to at least 30 MHz. The difference in high-frequency response between the two toroidal Baluns (with 50-ohm loads) is due to the differences in the lengths of their transmission lines. The transmission line on the powdered-iron core is appreciably less because the OD, as well as the cross-sectional area, is smaller.

4. The trifilar-wound form of the 1:1 Balun also has an additional undesirable property. Its high frequency response is sensitive to unbalanced and mismatched loads. This is because the third wire now forms two tightly coupled transmission lines. It is unlike the Ruthroff version shown on the right in **Photo 7-A**. In his second article,[12] Turrin pointed out this important distinction.

J. Reisert, W1JR—1978

The next significant article on 1:1 Baluns was published by Reisert in 1978.[7] Reisert proposed winding some of the smaller (but still high-powered) coaxial cables around a 2.4-inch OD ferrite toroid with a per-

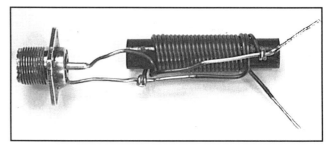

Photo 7-C. *A typical rod-type Balun.*

meability of 125. The windings also included a crossover, which is shown in **Figure 7-5** and **Photo 7-D**. In addition, he recommended various numbers of turns, depending upon the low-frequency requirement. For example, he suggested 12 turns to cover 3.5 MHz, 10 turns for 7 MHz, 6 for 14 MHz, and 4 for 21 and 28 MHz. Because the characteristic impedance of the coaxial cable is the same as the coax feedline, the Balun only introduces a foot or two of extra length to the feedline. This is true in the HF and VHF bands. The coaxial cables recommended in the article were RG-141/U, RG-142/U, and RG-303/U.

From the articles that followed in the amateur radio literature, it became apparent that few recognized all of the important features of Reisert's Balun. They are listed below.

1. An efficient, low-loss ferrite was used.

2. The Baluns had sufficient choking reactances for the various low-frequency requirements.

3. The characteristic impedance of the coiled transmission line was the same as that of the feedline, thus eliminating the extra transformer action of a length of transmission line with a different characteristic impedance.

4. The Balun is a form of Guanella's two-conductor 1:1 Balun, which is not prone to core flux and, hence, saturation and the generation of spurious frequencies. It is also not susceptible to mismatched and unbalanced loads as are the Turrin and "voltage" Baluns.

After constructing several of Reisert's Baluns and comparing them with other Guanella designs, I found that the crossover winding had virtually no effect up to 100 MHz (the limit of my equipment). In regards to Reisert's VSWR comparison with a rod-type Balun when feeding a triband Yagi beam on 20 meters, I found that his Balun had a lower VSWR (practically 1:1) at the best match point. The rod-type Balun had a best VSWR of about 1.3:1, but at a slightly higher frequency. He attributed the higher (and somewhat flatter) VSWR curve of the rod-type Balun to its greater ohmic loss. Because the rod-type Baluns I have investigated used the same low-loss ferrite that Reisert's did, I suspect that the differences in the VSWR curves were mainly due to the mismatch loss introduced by the rod-type Balun.

G. Badger, W6TC—1980

Badger published an in-depth, two-part series[13,14] in *Ham Radio* magazine in 1980 on air-core Baluns and Ununs. I am sure it was instrumental in advancing the technology of this class of wideband transformers. An article by Orr[15] also shows that there are many other radio amateurs who see the advantages of air-core transformers.

What are the claims for air-core Baluns over their ferrite-core counterparts? First and foremost, proponents of air-core Baluns claim they don't suffer the consequences of saturation that leads to spurious frequencies, heating, and ultimate damage. Secondly, it's said that they are not subject to arcing from the windings to the core.

What are the claims for the ferrite-core Baluns over their air-core counterparts? Simply put, they have wider bandwidths and are more compact.

After reading Badger's two-part series, I found that my curiosity was piqued by his experimental data on harmonic distortion due to saturation in a ferrite-core 1:1 Balun. Although many have expressed concerns regarding saturation in ferrite-core Baluns, Badger's

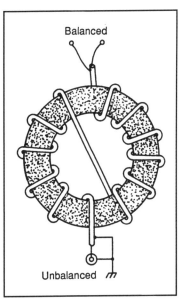

Figure 7-5. *A pictorial of the crossover used in Reisert's 1:1 Balun.*

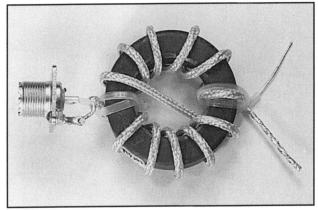

Photo 7-D. *A Reisert, W1JR, 1:1 Balun.*

data could very well provide the only results available. He used the two-tone test method, which combined two RF sources of 2.001 and 2.003 MHz, amplified it to 2 kW PEP and then fed it through a commercial 1:1 rod-type ferrite Balun. The data showed considerable distortion in the 3rd order and 9th order distortion products. In other words, appreciable nonlinearity took place at this high power level.

Several questions come to mind regarding these measurements. What was the low-frequency response of the commercial 1:1 rod-type Balun Badger used? From my measurements on a rod-type Balun (**Figure 7-4**), I found a drop in the input impedance and an inductive component at 2 MHz. This indicates flux in the core and a problem when using this Balun at 2 MHz. Because many rod-type 1:1 Baluns have been used over the years, it would have been instructive if he had also made these measurements at 4 and 7

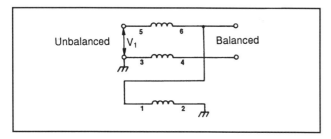

Figure 7-6. *Schematic of Badger's 1:1 Balun with a compensating winding (1-2). Winding (3-4) is the outer-braid of the coax and winding (5-6) is the inner conductor.*

MHz. They would have given the readers a safe lower-frequency limit for these Baluns.

I wondered why Badger didn't make similar measurements on Reisert's 1:1 Balun, which he included in his articles. As noted earlier, I consider Reisert's 1:1 Balun a very good design! I am sure that no distortion products would have been found at 2 MHz with this Balun. The end result is that Badger chose a poor ferrite-core design for making his comparisons. This helped to contribute to an undeserved reputation for the ferrite-core Balun.

Badger also suggested placing an insulated wire in parallel with the coax winding on Reisert's 1:1 Balun. He called this a compensating winding, which provided a superior balanced output. The third winding (1-2) is shown **Figure 7-6**. Winding (5-6) is the inner conductor and winding (3-4), the outer braid. Later experiments by myself and others have shown that a well-designed two conductor (Guanella) 1:1 Balun has a completely satisfactory balanced output for antenna applications. Furthermore, it does not suffer from an unbalanced and/or mismatched load and core saturation. Incidentally, Badger's schematic of **Figure 7-6** now adds up to four different versions of the 1:1 Balun. They are the two-conductor version of Guanella's and the three, three-conductor versions of Ruthroff's, Turrin's, and (now) Badger's.

Badger and Orr also mentioned the Collins Balun in their articles. This Balun is comprised of a dummy

length of coax wound as a continuation of the original coiled coax winding. Interestingly, it is connected as a Ruthroff 1:1 Balun (**Figure 7-2B**), which also uses a third winding. Because there is appreciable coupling between the two coiled windings, the Collins Balun should also be susceptible to mismatched and/or unbalanced loads. Badger claimed it was, by far, the best 1:1 Balun he had ever used. Again, it would have been very informative if he had compared it with the Reisert Balun (without the compensating third wire).

M.W. Maxwell, W2DU—1983

One of the more significant articles on 1:1 Baluns was published by Maxwell[4] in 1983. Maxwell introduced, what he called, the "choke" Balun. It was formed by placing high-permeability ferrite beads over about one foot of small (but high-powered) coaxial cables similar to the ones used in the Reisert Balun. **Photo 7-E** shows the W2DU "choke" Balun removed from its plastic enclosure.

Maxwell compared his Balun with (what he termed) a "transformer-type" Balun by measuring the input impedances versus frequency when the outputs were terminated in 50 ohms. The "transformer-type" Balun didn't yield a true 1:1 impedance transfer ratio, which he claimed was due to losses, leakage reactance, and less than optimum coupling. Because Maxwell gave no description of the "transformer-type" Balun, I assumed it was the popular rod-type Balun shown in **Photo 7-C**. As you can see in **Figure 7-4**, this Balun has a poor low-frequency response. Furthermore, it is really optimized for a load of 47 ohms and not 50 ohms.

What Maxwell failed to realize was that his Balun was a form of Guanella's two-conductor type. That is, it is both a choke (a lumped element) and a transmission line (a distributed element). Additionally, Guanella's theory applies whether the transmission lines are coiled (about a core) or beaded, twin-lead or coaxial cable. From Ruthroff's classic paper,[9] which extended Guanella's work,[3] we became aware of the

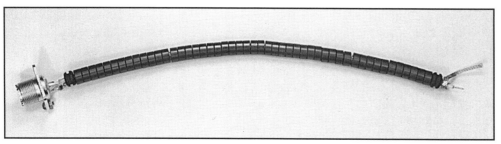

Photo 7-E. *The Maxwell, W2DU, "choke" 1:1 Balun.*

voltage drops along the lengths of the transmission lines. From very accurate insertion loss measurements,[2] we learned that the losses were mainly in the magnetic medium—and that they were related to the voltage levels and the permeabilities. Maxwell didn't take into account these latter findings. He used lossy high-permeability beads (2500) and assumed that the main loss was in the transmission line. He claimed that the CW power-handling capability of his Balun was 3.5 kW at 50 MHz and 9 kW at 10 MHz—the same as the coaxial cable itself. I seriously question these power ratings. Ironically, it is very likely that Maxwell's Balun had more real loss than the so-called "transformer-type" Balun!

R.W. Lewallen, W7EL—1985

There is very little doubt that Lewallen's interesting article[6] in 1985 contributed significantly to the better understanding and design of 1:1 and 4:1 Baluns. In it, he coined the (now very popular) terms "voltage" and "current" Baluns. The "voltage" Balun, a three-conductor type, has output ports which have voltages that are balanced to ground. It is brought about (see **Figure 7-6**) by the voltage-divider action of windings (5-6) and (1-2). Because we have two tightly coupled transmission lines in the passband with the same potential gradients, terminal 6 is at $+V_1/2$ and terminal 4 at $-V_1/2$ where V_1 is the input voltage. The "current" Balun, on the other hand, is a two-conductor Balun that produces equal and opposite currents on the output ports for any form of load impedance.

Lewallen conducted a series of experiments on 10 meters to compare the performances of "voltage" and "current" Baluns under balanced and unbalanced conditions. In the unbalanced (nonsymetrical) condition, the dipole was lengthened by five inches on one side and shortened by five inches on the other side. He then obtained a figure of merit for both Baluns (as well as for the case without a Balun) defined as the ratio of the average magnitude of the currents at the feedpoint over the magnitude of the imbalance (the inverted L) current. The magnitudes of the currents were obtained by current-probe toroids. Measurements were made at the antenna feedpoint and at a half-wave (physically) from it.

The "current" Balun consisted of 15 turns of very small RG-178/U coax on an FT82-61 core (a ferrite toroid with an OD of 0.825 inches and a permeability of 125). The "voltage" Balun had 10 turns of RG-178/U coax with a No. 26 wire in parallel (closely coupled) on the same toroid. The schematic is shown in **Figure 7-6**.

Lewallen concluded (and I agree) that his experiments clearly showed that the "current" Balun gave superior performance at every measured point in each experiment. However, the "voltage" Balun still improved the balance over the no-Balun case. He also concluded that other experiments should be performed in order to better compare the two forms of the Balun. One is to ascertain the difference when the feedline is placed nonsymetrical with respect to the antenna (to induce an imbalance current into the feedline). Others include determining the optimum point in the feedline to place the Balun, and testing the various kinds of core and beaded Baluns.

Although Lewallen's article pretty much speaks to Badger's proposal of adding a third wire to Reisert's Balun for better balance (i.e., avoid it), there are some comments and questions I have regarding his experiments and findings. They are:

1. Why didn't Lewallen use Reisert's Balun as the "current" Balun and Badger's suggested third-wire design as the "voltage" Balun? These would have been more realistic designs for comparisons. Instead, he used very small structures (which will only find use in QRP operations) and, as such, have higher frequency capabilities. Also, because the "voltage" Balun only had 10 turns (and hence a shorter transmission line and a poorer low-frequency response), it was favored in the comparisons on 10 meters. Had Lewallen used transmission lines of equal lengths on Reisert's cores, the differences between the two Baluns would have been even more dramatic.

2. It would also have been very useful if Lewallen had made comparisons between a "current" Balun that could handle the full legal limit of amateur radio power (again like the Reisert Balun) and "voltage" Baluns using Turrin's schematic (**Figure 7-3**) with rod and toroidal cores which have been readily available for nearly three decades.

3. Additionally, comparisons should not only be limited to 10 meters. Because 1:1 "voltage" Baluns are configurations of coupled transmission lines with various characteristic impedances, their performances with mismatched and unbalanced loads are more sensitive to the higher frequencies than their "current" Balun counterparts. Therefore, making similar measurements on 20 meters would also provide more useful information.

4. Even though Ruthroff's classic 1959 paper[9] has been the industry standard over the years, his 1:1

Balun design has been practically nonexistent in the amateur literature. Turrin mentioned its advantage over his first design in his second article.[12] But Turrin's first design has prevailed in our amateur literature. Because Ruthroff's design has the third conductor on a separate part of the toroid, it has the balanced output mentioned by Badger,[13] but still retains the flexibility of the Guanella[3] Balun. In other words, as the frequency is increased, the choking action of the third wire makes it practically transparent. This enables it to handle any form of load impedance. It would have been informative if Lewallen had pointed this out and also noted that Ruthroff's 1:1 Balun, although looking like a "voltage" Balun, is really a "current" Balun.

5. Lewallen and the others who have published in the amateur radio literature have failed to reference the first presentation on what are now known as "current" or "choke" Baluns, made by Guanella[3] in 1944. Even though Guanella used coiled transmission lines without a magnetic core, his theory on how these devices work is still applicable today.

J.S. Belrose, VE2CV—1991

The last article on 1:1 Baluns I considered worth mentioning was written by Belrose[5] in 1991. In it, he described the W2DU Balun by Maxwell and how his technique of threading coaxial cable through ferrite beads could be easily applied to 4:1 and 9:1 Baluns.

What immediately grabbed my attention in this article was the *deck head* (the editor's comments), which included highly complimentary remarks regarding the beaded-coax Balun. In essence, it said, "In this breakthrough article, W2DU's peerless 1:1 current-Balun design serves as the basis for excellent ferrite-bead-choke current Baluns capable of 4:1 and 9:1 impedance transformation."

However, if one reads the article carefully, it becomes apparent that this is not what Belrose said. His words were, "The *current Balun* of the *type* developed by Walt Maxwell, W2DU—a Balun consisting of ferrite beads slipped over a length of coaxial cable—is the best so far devised (italics mine)." He did not say that W2DU's Balun was "peerless." In fact, in the article he said just the opposite. He pointed out that the W2DU Balun's main disadvantage is that the beads are lossy at HF and heating becomes a concern when the transmitting power exceeds 125 watts! For high power (that is 1-kW CW), Belrose recommended Roehm's[16] designs, which use lower perme-

ability (850) beads nearest the Balun's balanced output (where most of the heating takes place).

However, I do question two of the advantages he claims for the W2DU Balun. They are:

1. Its excellent power-loss and impedance-versus-frequency characteristics are much superior to those of a bifilar current Balun wound on a ferrite toroid.

2. It has excellent power-handling capability, and can function quite satisfactorily when working into highly reactive loads. This is so because the magnetic flux produced by currents flowing on this Balun's wires cannot saturate its ferrite beads.

Belrose obtained evidence for advantage number 1 by comparing the input impedance and power loss versus frequency of the W2DU Balun with a commercial Balun when they were terminated in 50 ohms. The commercial Balun was a bifilar wound toroidal type used in a differential-T tuner. What Belrose failed to realize was that the commercial Balun had heavily insulated wires, resulting in a characteristic impedance greater than 100 ohms. Thus, he was actually comparing a 50-ohm transmission line with a longer line that had a characteristic impedance in excess of 100 ohms! As expected, his input impedance versus frequency curve for the commercial Balun was even more severe than that of the Turrin Balun shown in **Figure 7-4**.

Advantage number 2 is based upon the premise that the magnetic flux produced by currents on the W2DU Balun's wires cannot saturate the ferrite beads, while the windings of a bifilar wound toroidal current Balun can. This is an incorrect assumption because the magnetic flux of a two-conductor type Balun, like the beaded-coax or the bifilar-wound toroidal Balun, is generated by the imbalance (inverted L) current and hence is *much* lower than the transmission line currents. This is especially true with sufficient choking reactances. The perception that the toroidal type Balun still transmits the energy to the output circuit by flux linkages, could very well lead to this mistaken impression.

For high power beaded-coax Baluns, Belrose referred to designs by Roehm,[16] who increased the power capability of this type of Balun by using lower permeability beads near the balanced output. He also increased the length considerably. For operation from 80 meters to 10 meters, Roehm used 28 inches of beaded coax. For 160 meters to 10 meters, he used 36 inches of beaded coax. Belrose's suggestion of connecting beaded coaxes in parallel on the low-imped-

Photo 7-F. *Two versions of Reisert's 1:1 Balun. The Balun on the left uses the crossover shown in Figure 7-5. The Balun on the right is continuously wound. Both have the same electrical performance in the HF band.*

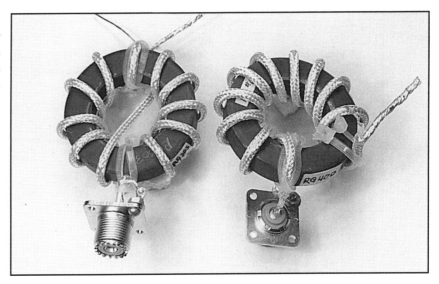

ance side and in series on the high impedance side to obtain a broadband 4:1 transformation ratio would require transmission lines with characteristic impedances of 100 ohms. This means, for a high power 4:1 Balun using beaded transmission lines, about 56 inches of beaded line would be required for the 80-meter to 10-meter operation and 72 inches for the 160-meter to 10-meter coverage. For a 9:1 Balun, it would be necessary to increase these lengths by 50 percent!

It remains to be seen what Belrose would have said or done if he had compared the W2DU Balun of Maxwell's with the W1JR Balun of Reisert's. He certainly couldn't claim the advantages listed in his article for the W2DU Balun. Would he still have claimed that the type of Balun developed by Maxwell is the best so far devised? Given the evidence, I doubt it.

Sec 7.4   High-, Medium-, and Low-power Designs

In this section I'll present my latest 1:1 Balun designs. Except for one Balun that appeared in the June 1993 issue of *CQ*, the others appeared for the first time in the magazine's April 1994 issue. Because I have favored Reisert's design throughout this chapter, the first Baluns described here are my versions of his technique of coiling small (but high power) coaxial cable around a low-permeability ferrite toroid. For my wire versions, I could have used all sorts of adjectives to describe them like Guanella, two-conductor, choke, and current. However, in the process of writing this section, I thought Belrose's adjectives were the most direct. Using his words, I call my wire versions of the 1:1 Balun simply—*bifilar toroidal Baluns*.

Photo 7-F shows two versions of Reisert's Balun. The one on the left uses the crossover shown in **Figure 7-5**. Because no difference in performance at HF was noticed without the crossover, a continuous-wound version is also shown on the right. The main advantage in the HF band with the crossover winding is purely mechanical. Having the input and output connections on opposite sides of the toroid is not only more convenient, but it also offers a much stronger method of mounting.

For operation from 1.8 to 30 MHz, 10 turns of small coax like RG-303/U, RG-142B/U, or RG-400/U are wound on a 2.4-inch OD ferrite toroid with a permeability of 250. If the use is limited from 3.5 to 30 MHz, then a permeability of 125 is recommended because it would yield a slightly higher efficiency at the high end. If one wants the highest possible efficiency and limits the operation from 14 to 30 MHz, then a permeability of 40 is recommended. With loads grounded at their centers, these conditions were found to give ample margins (handle a VSWR of 3:1 without any appreciable flux) at their low frequency ends.

For ease of winding, I found TY-RAP™ Cable Ties *very* useful. Two were used at each end. Removing the covering on the outer braid also helps. Because about 24 inches of cable is wound on the toroid, I recommend you start with at least 32 inches. Of the three cables noted above, I found RG-303/U cable the easiest to wind and connect. Although it only has a single-thickness braid (the others have double-thickness braids), its power rating is still the same—9 kW at 10 MHz and 3.5 kW at 50 MHz.

The next high power design is shown in **Photo 7-G** mounted in a 4 inch long by 3 inch wide by 2.25 inch

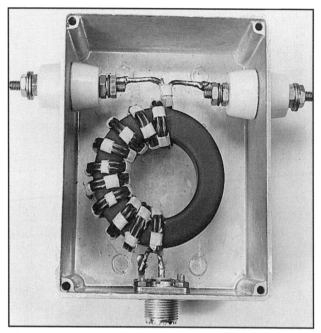

Photo 7-G. *My high-power design of a bifilar toroidal (Guanella/current) 1:1 Balun mounted in a 4 inch long by 3 inch wide by 2.25 inch high Bud aluminum box.*

high Bud CU 234 aluminum box. It has 10 bifilar turns of No. 12 H Thermaleze wire on a 2.4-inch OD ferrite toroid. As with the Reisert versions, a permeability of 250 is recommended for 1.8 to 30 MHz, 125 for 3.5 to 30 MHz, and 40 for 14 to 30 MHz. One wire is also covered with two layers of Scotch No. 92 polyimide tape in order to raise the characteristic impedance to 50 ohms. With this added insulation, the voltage breakdown of this twin-lead transmission line compares very favorably with RG-8/U cable (4000 volts). In order to preserve the spacing, the wires are also clamped together about every 1/2 inch with strips of Scotch No. 27 glass tape 3/16 inches wide and a little over 1 inch long.

Two "economy" versions of the high power bifilar toroidal Balun are shown in **Photo 7-H**. The one on the left shows the windings crowded on one-half of the toroid. The one on the right provides the same positions of the input and output connections by using the crossover. Their performances are identical. Both Baluns have 10 bifilar turns of No. 14 H Thermaleze wire on a 2.4-inch OD ferrite toroid. The choices of permeability, which trade off bandwidth for efficiency, are the same as those used in the two previous high power designs. The word "economy" here refers to economy in labor—this Balun is actually very easy to construct.

This "economy" Balun, which also handles the full legal limit of amateur radio power, has a small trade-off in high frequency response. Because no extra insulation is used, the characteristic impedance of two tightly clamped No. 14 H Thermaleze wires is 45 ohms. With one layer of Scotch No. 92 tape, it increases to 50 ohms. But for most of the HF band, the difference in performance between Baluns using transmission lines of 45 and 50 ohms should be negligible. Even without the extra insulation, the voltage breakdown should compare very favorably with the smaller, high-power coaxes used in the Reisert versions (1900 volts).

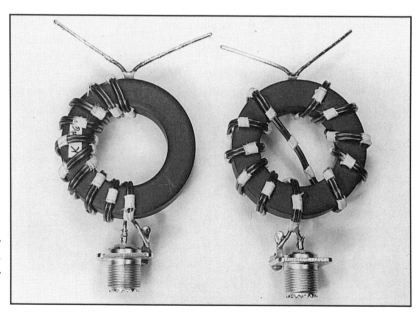

Photo 7-H. *Two "economy" versions of the high-power bifilar toroidal (Guanella/current) 1:1 Balun. The one on the right uses Reisert's crossover technique.*

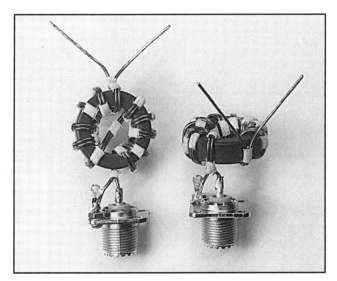

Photo 7-I. *Two low-power versions of the bifilar toroidal (Guanella/current) 1:1 Balun capable of handling the output of practically any HF transceiver. The Balun on the left has the crossover.*

Photo 7-J. *Two medium-power versions of the bifilar toroidal (Guanella/current) 1:1 Balun capable of handling the full legal limit of amateur radio power when the VSWR is less than 2:1. The Balun on the left has the crossover.*

Photo 7-I shows two low-power versions of a bifilar toroidal Balun capable of handling the output of practically any HF transceiver. One has a crossover winding and the other, a continuous winding. They both have 10 bifilar turns of No. 16 H Thermaleze wire on a 1.25-inch OD ferrite toroid with a permeability of 250. Since efficiency is not a major problem in low-power use, I found no reason to suggest the other two versions, which use lower permeabilities. It is also interesting to note that two tightly clamped No. 16 H Thermaleze wires have a characteristic impedance close to 50 ohms. Therefore, this small Balun (particularly with its short leads) has a very good high frequency response.

Photo 7-J shows two medium-power versions of a bifilar toroidal Balun capable of handling the full legal limit of amateur radio power under controlled conditions—when the VSWR is less than 2:1. Being smaller than its larger (2.4-inch OD) counterpart, its heat-sinking capability and, hence, power rating is less. As before, one Balun uses a crossover while the other doesn't. Each has 8 bifilar turns of No. 14 H Thermaleze wire on a 1.5-inch OD ferrite toroid. The ferrite permeabilities and expected bandwidths are the same as the other high-power Baluns. Because the average magnetic path length in the core is about two-thirds that of the 2.4-inch core, only 8 bifilar turns are required in order to produce a similar low-frequency capability. Even though the characteristic impedances

of their bifilar windings are 45 ohms, their responses on 10 meters should be somewhat better than the "economy" models because the lengths of their transmission lines are shorter (18 compared to 24 inches).

And now a few words on what sort of efficiency one can expect in trading-off low frequency response by using lower permeability ferrite cores. From earlier studies,[2] it was found that the efficiency (with sufficient choking, so only transmission line currents flow) is related to the permeability, the voltage drop along the length of the transmission line, and the frequency. The higher the permeability and/or voltage drop, the greater the loss. Additionally, the higher the permeability, the greater the loss with frequency. It was also found that a permeability of less than 300 was necessary in order to obtain the very high efficiencies of which these devices are capable.

Here are some efficiencies that might be expected from ferrites under matched conditions, based on the results of the studies:

1. With 250 material, an efficiency near 99 percent at 1.8 MHz and 97 percent at 30 MHz.

2. With 125 material, an efficiency near 99 percent at 3.5 MHz and 98 percent at 30 MHz.

3. With 40 material, an efficiency of 99 percent at 14 MHz and at 30 MHz.

When a Balun is exposed to a high impedance resulting in a VSWR of 2:1, the voltage, and hence loss, increases by about 40 percent. With a VSWR of

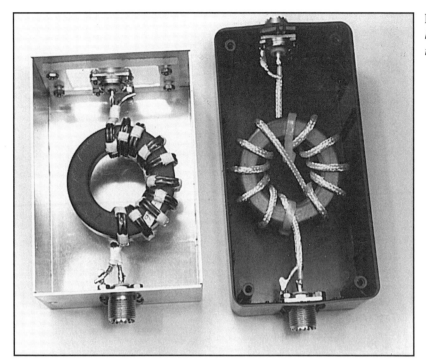

Photo 7-K. *Two examples of mounting the high-power 1:1 Guanella Balun in enclosures that allow isolation transformer operation.*

4:1, the loss doubles. With a VSWR of 10:1, the loss is more than three-fold. Since limited data was obtained in this study,[2] these increases in losses with increases in VSWR could very well be even greater.

Sec 7.5   Isolation Transformers

As was shown in the preceding sections, the 1:1 Guanella (current/choke) Balun is in reality a two-conductor RF choke, or an isolation transformer. However, practical Balun designs don't usually lend themselves to isolation use for mechanical reasons. They cannot be conveniently inserted into a coaxial cable system. Therefore, the objective is to mount the "Guanella Baluns" in enclosures that will allow them to perform as isolation transformers.

Photo 7-K shows two examples of enclosures that should accomplish the mission. The example on the left shows one of the high-power units mounted in a 5 inch long by 3.5 inch wide by 2.25 inch high aluminum enclosure. The output connector (on the top) is insulated by a 0.125-inch-thick piece of plastic. The one on the right shows another high-power unit mounted in a 6 inch long by 3 inch wide by 2 inch high plastic enclosure, which is available from Radio-Shack. The descriptions of the high-power units are given in the preceding section.

These isolation transformers can be used as Baluns when inserted in a coaxial cable one-half wavelength (physically) from a half-wave dipole[6] or between a

coaxial cable and a balanced L-C tuner.[16] They should never be inserted in a coaxial cable system that presents a high impedance and, consequently, a high voltage. This could be harmful to the unit.

Note that the high-power unit on the left in **Photo 7-K** can also be used as a filament choke in a Class B linear amplifier. Its low-frequency response is much better than any rod-type, assuring 160-meter operation. Obviously, it would not be mounted in the aluminum enclosure shown in the photo. In addition, the two layers of Scotch No. 92 tape would not be required because the characteristic impedance of the winding is unimportant and the voltages involved are quite low.

By the way, the designs discussed above can be used as phase-inverters. Simply connect the hot lead on one side to the ground on the other side.

Sec 7.6   Summary

In investigating the 1:1 Balun, I was quite surprised to see the ferrite- and powdered-iron-core designs that have been available in the literature and off-the-shelf since 1964. They not only had poor low- and high-frequency responses, but they were also susceptible to flux in the cores at their low-frequency ends. Furthermore, since they only used single-coated wires, they were also prone to voltage breakdown. No doubt, these designs are responsible for the poor reputation that the Balun has had for many years.

It wasn't until 1978, when Reisert published his article, that a Balun which had all of the attributes of a good design became available. Namely:

a) It is efficient because it uses a low-permeability core.

b) It has sufficient choking reactance to meet its low-frequency requirement.

c) It is not prone to flux in the core (and, hence, saturation) because it has no third winding.

d) It has a 50-ohm characteristic impedance and maintains a 1:1 transformation ratio with a 50-ohm load.

e) It has a good voltage breakdown capability (1900 volts).

f) It can handle a mismatched and/or unbalanced load.

However, succeeding investigators failed to see the advantages of Reisert's design and proposed their own. Surprisingly, they belonged to two distinct groups. One group favored "air-core" Baluns and the other, "choke" (beaded-coax) Baluns.

The main argument given by the "air-core" followers was that their Balun would never experience problems with saturation, while the "ferrite-core" Balun would. However, the Reisert Balun is a current/choke type Balun that could only have flux in the core due to the imbalance (inverted L) current, which is much smaller than the transmission line currents. In fact, with any degree of choking reactance by the coiled transmission line, the imbalance current is essentially negligible. Therefore, saturation is not a concern with a Balun like Reisert's. In all fairness, it should be noted that it is a different story with the 4:1 current/choke and voltage Baluns. All three of these types of Baluns have a "magnetizing inductance" in their low-frequency models and hence a possibility of saturation with a poor design.

The advocates of the "choke" 1:1 Balun claim that their beaded-coax Balun can't saturate while the bifilar (current) toroidal Balun can. This is untrue; they are basically the same kind of structure, and neither has a third conductor which could allow a flux-causing current at the very low-frequency end. But of all of the attributes listed above for the Reisert Balun, the first one has the "choke" Balun at a disadvantage in the HF band. Because its transmission line is not coiled about a toroid, it does not have the multiplication factor of N^2 (due to mutual coupling), where N is the number of turns, while the toroidal Balun does. Therefore, higher-permeability beads are required in order to obtain sufficient choking reactance. This results in lower efficiency.

Finally, it should be pointed out that the 1:1 Balun using the small, but high-power, coaxial cable is capable of 5-kW operation in the HF band. Because of current crowding, the bifilar toroidal Balun, even with No. 12 wire, has shown excessive wire heating at this level. Therefore, No. 10 or No. 8 wire, with added layers of Scotch No. 92 tape in order to obtain a 50-ohm characteristic impedance, is recommended.

Chapter **8**

The 4:1 Balun

Sec 8.1   Introduction

Chapter 7 in this book discussed the most popular of all Baluns—the 1:1 Balun designed to match 50 ohms unbalanced to 50 ohms balanced. It not only gave a review of the history, theory, and design of these broadband transformers, but also my viewpoint on published articles advocating later designs using coaxial cable wound around a toroid, threaded through ferrite beads, or just plain coiled in air (an air-core Balun). As was noted, I am in considerable disagreement with many of the claims advanced for these later 1:1 Baluns.

Chapter 8 deals with the next most popular Balun—the 4:1 Balun designed to match 50 ohms unbalanced to 200 ohms balanced. Baluns matching 50 ohms unbalanced to 12.5 ohms balanced are also included. It begins with a little information on the history and design of these Baluns, followed by high- and low-power designs and comparisons with other Baluns that have been on the market or in the amateur literature. Guanella's approach to the design of a 4:1 Balun is particularly noteworthy. It not only yields an excellent Balun design, but also an Unun (unbalanced-to-unbalanced transformer) with practically the same performance. His design could very well be called a *Balun/Unun*. As in the first chapter, this one also closes with a brief summary of the significant points.

Sec 8.2   A Little History and Design Information

There are really only two classic papers that have established the principles upon which the transmission line transformer (the Balun being a subset thereof) is based. The first one was written by Guanella in 1944. Guanella proposed the idea of coiling a transmission line to isolate the input from the output, resulting in the (now popular) *current* or *choke*

Balun.[3] The second was by Ruthroff in 1959, whose analysis of these transmission line transformers is the present industry standard.[9] Ruthroff also introduced the Unun and the hybrid transformer.

Interestingly enough, both Guanella and Ruthroff had different approaches to their 1:1 and 4:1 Balun designs. Guanella used a two-conductor 1:1 Balun design, while Ruthroff used a three-conductor design. Ruthroff's third conductor (which was said to increase the low-frequency response over the two-conductor Balun[12]) lay on a separate part of a toroidal core. Investigators who followed failed to recognize this fact. Their comparisons were made with a three-conductor Balun that had the third wire in parallel with the other two, which then formed two coupled transmission lines. This gave rise to the term *voltage* Balun—an inferior design.[6]

However, the differences between Guanella's and Ruthroff's approaches to 4:1 Baluns were even more striking. Guanella connected coiled transmission lines in a parallel-series arrangement, so in-phase voltages were summed at the high impedance side. His Balun has been called a *current* Balun.[6] Ruthroff, on the other hand, obtained a 4:1 transformation ratio by summing a direct voltage with a delayed voltage that traversed a single transmission line in a phase-inverter connection (see **Chapter 7**). His Balun has been called a *voltage* Balun. The distinction between the operation of these two Baluns was also overlooked by practically everyone who followed.

This section reviews the two different approaches taken by Guanella and Ruthroff in obtaining 4:1 Baluns. Of particular importance are the descriptions of the potential drops along the lengths of the transmission lines when the loads are grounded at various points. These voltage drops are not only relevant to the ohmic losses in the Baluns, but also to their electrical performances. These descriptions were quite

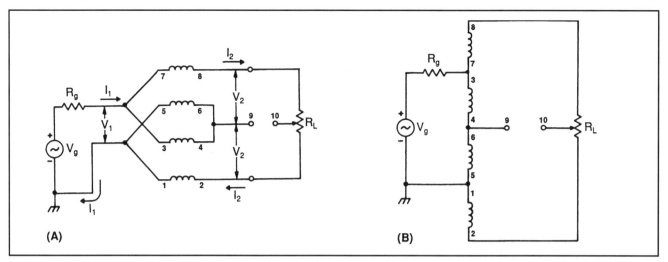

Figure 8-1. *Electrical models of the Guanella 4:1 Balun: (A) high-frequency, (B) low-frequency.*

possibly presented for the first time in the second edition of my book *Transmission Line Transformers*.[2]

Sec 8.2.1 Guanella's 4:1 Balun

Figures 8-1A and **B** show the high- and low-frequency models of Guanella's method of connecting transmission lines in parallel-series to obtain a 4:1 Balun. The high-frequency model (**Figure 8-1A**) assumes that the choking reactances of the coiled (or beaded) transmission lines are sufficient to isolate the input from the output, so only transmission line currents are allowed to flow. This occurs when the reactance of windings 3-4 and 5-6 (which are in series) is much greater than R_g (at least by a factor of ten).[2] If two cores are used, the reactance is the sum of the reactances of windings 3-4 and 5-6. If a single core is used, the reactance is twice as large because of the mutual coupling between the windings. The other advantage of Guanella's method (besides only using one core) is that shorter transmission lines can be used, resulting in better high-frequency performance.

As with all transmission line transformers, the objective is to have the transmission lines see loads equal to their characteristic impedances, resulting in "flat lines." This yields the highest frequency response. Because each transmission line in **Figure 8-1A** sees one half of the load, R_L, the optimum value of the characteristic impedance is $R_L/2$. Consequently, the input impedance, V_1/I_1, is simply the impedance of two identical transmission lines connected in parallel. It follows that the impedance transformation ratio is the load, R_L, divided by the input impedance.

Because the Guanella 4:1 Balun sums voltages of equal delays from identical transmission lines, his Balun is only limited in high-frequency performance by the deviation of the characteristic impedance of the transmission lines from the optimum values and the parasitics not absorbed into the characteristic impedance of the lines. I (and practically everyone else) had overlooked the simple and important statement, "a frequency independent transformation," which appeared in Guanella's 1944 article[3]—a fact that is evidenced by the scarcity of his designs in the literature. Another interesting aspect of the Guanella 4:1 Balun is the analysis of his Balun when the load is floating or grounded at different points. This leads to the determination of the voltage gradients that exist along the transmission lines and the various functions of which his 4:1 design is capable. Assuming a matched load or very short transmission lines resulting in $V_2 = V_1$, they are as follows.

Floating Load

With terminal 10 (which is at the center of R_L) floating, the potential gradient along the top transmission line in **Figure 8-1A** (windings 5-6 and 7-8) is $-1/2V_1$; along the bottom transmission line (winding 1-2 and 3-4) it's $-3/2V_1$. The voltage to ground on terminal 9, V_{90}, is $-1/2V_1$. Because the bottom transmission line (in **Figure 8-1A**) has a voltage drop along its length three times greater than the top transmission line, it results in three times more loss because losses in transmission line transformers are voltage dependent (dielectric-type losses).[2]

Even though a single-core Guanella 4:1 Balun maintains the voltages (stated above) when feeding a folded dipole (of about 200 ohms) which has a virtual-ground potential at terminal 10, it still feeds equal currents to each side of the antenna because of the series-connection at its output. Since the output voltages are not balanced to ground, a reactive component is probably introduced into the input impedance. Additionally, the choking reactance of the windings also prevents antenna currents from flowing on the outside of the coaxial cable feedline.

Load Grounded at Center

When two cores are used and terminal 10 (the center of R_L) is grounded, the voltage gradient along the top transmission line in **Figure 8-1A** is zero, and along the bottom transmission line it is $-V_1$. The voltage to ground on terminal 9 (V_{90}) is also zero. In fact, the core for the top transmission line isn't needed. It merely acts as a mechanical support for the top transmission line, which now only operates as a delay line. Also, all of the loss now occurs in the core of the bottom transmission line where a longitudinal potential gradient exists. Furthermore, the low-frequency response, as seen from **Figure 8-1B**, is now determined by the reactances of windings 1-2 and 3-4. This means that the low-frequency response with a floating load is better by a factor of two over the case where the load is grounded at its center.

But the single-core case is a different matter. Since the potential at terminal 9 (V_{90}) wants to be at $-1/2V_1$, connecting a ground directly to the center of R_L causes an imbalance that renders the single-core Balun unusable. If the ground were placed at a point 25 percent below terminal 8 (50 ohms from terminal 8 with a 200-ohm load), no difference would be noted

from a floating load. This condition also exists when two cores are used.

Load Grounded at the Bottom

It is when the load is grounded at the bottom (at terminal 2), that we have what is probably the most interesting case. The 4:1 Balun (with two cores) is now converted into a very broadband Unun (unbalanced-to-unbalanced transformer). Because the bottom transmission line in **Figure 8-1A** has no potential drop along its length, it only acts as a delay line. The voltage to ground at terminal 9 (V_{90}) is $+V_1$, and the voltage gradient along the top transmission line is $+V_1$. This results in a voltage of $2V_1$ across the load. The low-frequency response is now determined by the reactances of windings 5-6 and 7-8. This is just the opposite of the Balun case when the center of the load was grounded. A single-core 4:1 Guanella Balun can also be converted to an Unun by putting a 1:1 Balun (for isolation) in series with the 4:1 Balun.[2]

There is a reason for claiming a very broadband response for a Guanella Unun (converted from his Balun)—the two in-phase voltages are now summed at the high-impedance side. The only other competition for a 4:1 Unun design is that of Ruthroff's,[9] where a direct voltage is summed with a delayed voltage that traversed a single transmission line (and, hence, had a built-in, high-frequency cut-off). In fact, very little information can be found in the literature on a *Guanella 4:1 Unun.*

Sec 8.2.2   Ruthroff's 4:1 Balun

Figures 8-2A and **B** show the high- and low-frequency models of Ruthroff's approach for a 4:1 Balun. The high-frequency model (**Figure 8-2A**) assumes that the

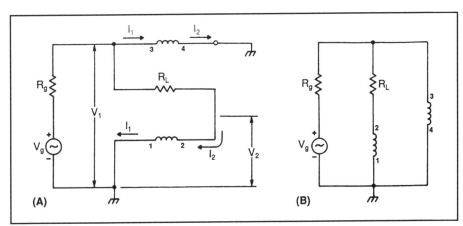

Figure 8-2. *Electrical models of the Ruthroff 4:1 Balun: (A) high-frequency, (B) low-frequency.*

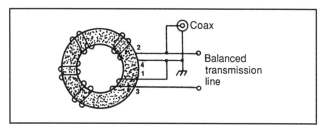

Figure 8-3. *A pictorial of the connections for a 4:1 Ruthroff (voltage) Balun.*

choking reactance of the coiled (or beaded) transmission line is sufficient to isolate the input from the output, so only transmission line currents are allowed to flow. This occurs when the reactance of winding 3-4 (or 1-2, because they are the same) is much greater than R_g (at least by a factor of ten[2]).

As **Figure 8-2A** indicates, the transmission line is connected in a *phase-inverter* function (see **Chapter 7**). That is, a $-V_1$ voltage gradient now exists along the length of the transmission line. Therefore, the voltage across R_L now becomes $V_1 + V_2$. Although Ruthroff analyzed his 4:1 Unun in his classic paper,[9] his results also apply to his Balun with a floating load, because both devices sum a direct voltage with a delayed voltage. In essence, he used loop equations on the input and output and transmission line equations to eliminate one set of variables (I_2 and V_2). Ruthroff also used a maxima technique (setting a derivative to zero) to solve for the optimum characteristic impedance of the transmission line. As in the Guanella case, he found the optimum value to be $1/2R_L$.

An inspection of **Figure 8-2A** shows that the left side of R_L (terminal 3) has a direct voltage (V_1) to ground, and the right side (terminal 2) a delayed voltage ($-V_2$) to ground, which traveled the length of the transmission line. Also note, that if the line is electrically one-half wavelength long, the output is *zero*. As a result, Ruthroff's design (which has a built-in cut-off) is sensitive to the transmission line length.

I have recently unearthed another interesting aspect of Ruthroff's design.[2] If the center of the load is grounded, the high-frequency performance is vastly improved. The built-in high-frequency cut-off is eliminated and the Balun appears to take on the character of a Guanella Balun that sums voltages of equal delays. A closer inspection reveals that the input impedance now consists of two impedances in parallel: one consisting of $R_L/2$, and the other of a "flat line" terminated by $R_L/2$. As a result, the currents are not in phase!

Surprisingly, when matching into a folded dipole with an input impedance of 200 ohms, Ruthroff's Balun exhibits a high frequency response that is much greater than expected (see later sections). Because the folded dipole has a *virtual* ground at its center, the Balun could very well be summing voltages of equal phases.

Sec 8.2.3   Amateur Radio History and Design

Looking back at old issues of amateur radio handbooks (I don't have a complete set), I found that the first presentation on broadband 4:1 Baluns appeared in the 1955 edition of *The ARRL Handbook*. The section was called "Coil Baluns." The schematic diagram was that of Guanella's, shown in **Figure 8-1A**. What surprised me was that this section appeared to use many of the important words contained in Guanella's article.[3] It mentioned that the choking action of the coiled transmission lines should be great enough to isolate the input from the output at the lowest frequency of interest. It also included the requirement on the characteristic impedance of the coiled transmission lines; namely, that the characteristic impedance should be equal to $R_L/2$, where R_L is the load.

However, the section also included two other statements which are not correct in light of today's design practices. One recommended that the length of the winding in each coil be equal to about a quarter wavelength. The other stated that the principal application is in going from a 300-ohm balanced load to a 75-ohm coaxial line. With magnetic cores, the lengths of the windings are now considerably shorter than a quarter wavelength, and the applications include a host of different impedance levels.

Recent issues of the handbooks now include the 4:1 broadband *coil Balun* (along with the same write-up that appeared in the 1955 issue), and one with windings on ferrite cores. They are now called 4:1 air-core current Baluns and "just plain" 4:1 current Baluns (ferrite cores being assumed). Unfortunately, what is lacking in the description of the 4:1 current Balun is information on the importance of the characteristic impedance of the windings and the value of the permeability of the ferrite cores. The literature states that 8 to 10 turns (of No. 14 Formvar-coated, close-spaced—I guess) on a toroidal core or 10 to 15 turns on a rod are typical values for the HF range. Ferrites with permeabilities from 850 to 2500 are also suggested. Nothing is mentioned regarding the dimensions of the cores.

In essence, there's very little information available today in our handbooks that would help one understand and construct the "popular" *current* Balun. Even the choices of recommended ferrites to be used are found wanting. Accurate loss measurements[2] have shown ferrites with permeabilities of 850 to 2500 to be lossy in Balun and Unun applications. Only when the permeabilities of ferrites are 300 or less will Baluns and Ununs exhibit the very high efficiencies of which they are capable.

Even though the 4:1 *voltage* Balun has actually had a shorter history than the *current* Balun, considerably more construction detail (including an actual photograph) has been available in the amateur radio handbooks. As far as I can tell, the first presentation took place between 1965 and 1968. In looking through succeeding issues (including the 1993 issue), I find the write-up hasn't changed much (if any) over the years. The 4:1 Balun from the handbooks and a commercial rod-type are described and compared with my designs in the succeeding sections.

Sec 8.3   4:1 Ruthroff Balun Designs

As mentioned above, the schematic of Ruthroff's Balun is shown in **Figure 8-2A**. A pictorial representation is shown in **Figure 8-3**. **Photo 8-A** (on the left) shows my construction of a design close to the one shown in the handbook's photographs. It has 10 close-spaced, bifilar turns of No. 14 Formvar-coated wire on a 2.4-inch OD ferrite toroid with a permeability of 40. **Figure 8-4** shows a plot of the input impedance versus frequency when the 200-ohm load is center-tapped-to-ground (which is close to the actual case when matching into balanced antenna systems). As you can see, when compared to a design that has the proper characteristic impedance of the winding and sufficient choking, the response is very poor. Although this Balun has been rated at 1000 watts of RF power from 1.8 through 60 MHz, I would suggest it not be used below 6 MHz for fear of excessive flux in the core (especially when the magnitude of the load is greater than 200 ohms). Also, above 14 MHz, the transformation becomes considerably greater than 4:1.

My design, on the right in **Photo 8-A**, has 14 bifilar turns of No. 14 tinned copper wire on a 2.4-inch OD ferrite toroid with a permeability of 125 or 250. The wires are threaded through No. 13 Teflon tubing with

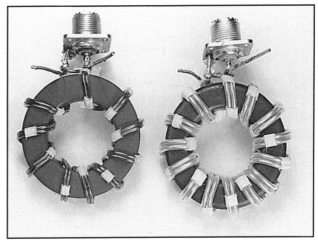

Photo 8-A. *Two designs of the 4:1 Ruthroff (voltage) Balun. The one on the left is taken from the amateur radio handbook. The one on the right is my improved version.*

a wall thickness of 20 mils. As you can see by its excellent high frequency response in **Figure 8-4**, the characteristic impedance of the bifilar winding must be very close to the ideal value of 100 ohms. **Photo 8-B** shows two different views of my design mounted in a 4 inch long by 3 inch wide by 2.25 inch high Bud CU 234 aluminum box. The Balun, which is placed equidistant between the top, bottom, and sides of the enclosure, is securely mounted by soldering its leads to the two feedthrough insulators and the SO-239 chassis connector.

It should be mentioned that if the Balun is to be used mainly on the lower portion of the HF band (including 160 meters), then the 250 permeability ferrite is recommended. Even though the difference in low frequency response between permeabilities of 125 and 250 doesn't show up in **Figure 8-4**, the 250 permeability would provide an extra safety margin (from flux in the core) at the low frequency end. The trade-off lies in giving up a little in efficiency (about 1 percent) for an increase in the safety margin (a factor of 2) at the low end.

Incidentally, the handbooks also state that the Balun can be used between a balanced 300-ohm point and a 75-ohm unbalanced line. Because I suspected this statement as well, I again measured the input impedances versus frequency of both Baluns when terminated in a 300-ohm center-tapped-to-ground load. **Figure 8-5** shows the deterioration that takes place, especially at the high end. Even a Balun that is well designed for a 50:200-ohm impedance level is not recommended

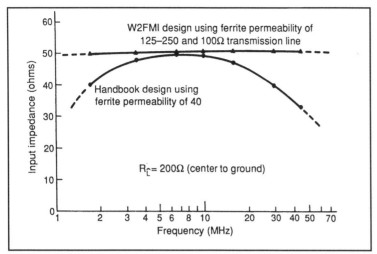

Figure 8-4. *The input impedance versus frequency for a 4:1 Ruthroff (voltage) Balun design from the amateur radio handbook and one optimized for the 50:200-ohm level. The load is grounded at its center.*

Figure 8-5. *The input impedance versus frequency for the two Ruthroff Baluns of Figure 8-4, but with a 300-ohm load. Note the deterioration of the W2FMI design, which was optimized for the 50:200-ohm level.* ↓

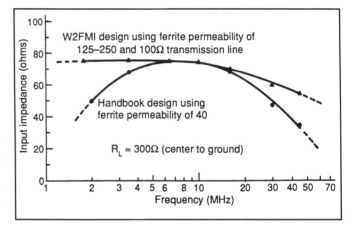

for the 75:300-ohm level. Because the length of the transmission line becomes significant beyond 10 MHz, standing waves then change the impedance ratio due to the mismatch with the Balun's transmission line. My design also shows more safety margin at the low end. I'm surprised that these simple measurements weren't made many years ago.

However, the Balun shown in the handbook does have one interesting feature. It uses a very low permeability ferrite (40), which has been shown by very accurate insertion loss measurements[2] to yield efficiencies in Baluns (and Ununs) of *99 percent* at the

Photo 8-B. *Two different views of the optimized version of the 4:1 Ruthroff Balun mounted in a 4 inch long by 3 inch wide by 2.25 inch high Bud CU 234 aluminum enclosure.*

50:200-ohm impedance level! This is even a percent or two better than the ferrite with a permeability of 125. Because this ferrite permeability is so low, the major problem lies in obtaining sufficient choking reactance at the lowest frequency of interest, so that only transmission line currents are allowed to flow.

The design chosen (in order to exploit this very high efficiency) is shown **Photo 8-C**. It uses 14 bifilar turns of the same wire, as with my previous Balun shown on the right in **Photo 8A**, on two 2.4-inch OD cores (bound together with No. 27 glass tape) with permeabilities of 40. The unmounted view shows how the two cores are bound together by glass tape. The other views attempt to give an example for mounting the Balun. The Balun is supported by two acrylic end pieces which are, in turn, held fast to the enclosure by a long bolt. The Balun is placed equidistant between the top, bottom, and sides of a 5 inch long by 3.5 inch wide by 2.25 inch high aluminum enclosure. A few washers at the point where the bolt comes through the enclosure help to position the Balun between the top and bottom.

When matching 50 ohms (unbalanced) to 200 ohms (balanced), the response of this Balun is practically the same as mine, shown in **Figure 8-4** using a single core. From 1.7 to 30 MHz, it can certainly handle the full legal limit of amateur radio power with an efficiency close to 99 percent. However, if the operation of this Balun is restricted to the HF band only (that is, from 3 to 30 MHz), then it could be rated conservatively at 10 kW of peak power and 5 kW of average power. It would be an ideal Balun for a log-periodic beam antenna.

Finally, **Photo 8-D** shows three different views of a low power 4:1 Ruthroff (voltage) Balun designed to handle the output power of any HF transceiver easily. It has 10 bifilar turns of No. 18 hook-up wire on a 1.5-inch OD ferrite toroid with a permeability of 250. The enclosure is a 2.75 inch long by 2.125 inch wide by 1.625 inch high CU 3000-A minibox.

Section 8.4   4:1 Guanella Balun Designs

Photo 8-E shows two high-power Guanella 4:1 Baluns designed to match 50-ohm coaxial cable to loads of 200 ohms. They both use No.14 H Thermaleze wire with a covering of Teflon tubing giving characteristic impedances very close to 100 ohms (the objective). Their responses are flat from 1.5 MHz

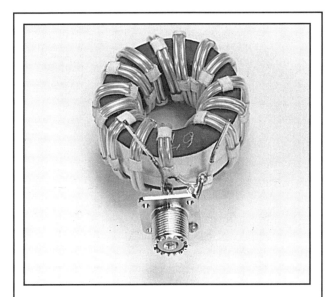

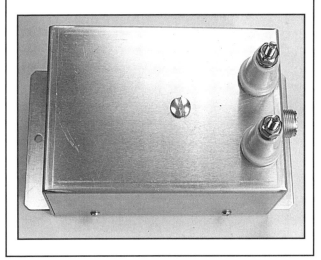

Photo 8-C. *Three views of the very high-power 4:1 Ruthroff Balun using two low-permeability (40) ferrite cores. Dimensions of the aluminum enclosure are: length, 5 inches; width, 3.5 inches; height, 2.25 inches.*

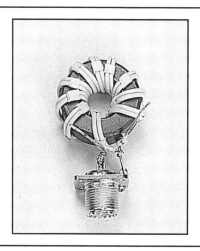

Photo 8-D. *Three views of the low-power 4:1 Ruthroff Balun designed to handle the output of any HF transceiver. The aluminum enclosure is a 2.75 inches high by 2.125 inches wide by 1.625 inches high CU 3000-A minibox.*

to well beyond 30 MHz. Both can easily handle the full legal limit of amateur radio power.

The single-core version (on the left) has 8 bifilar turns on each of its two transmission lines. The dual-core version (on the right) has 16 turns on each core. The wires are clamped together with strips of Scotch No. 27 glass tape placed about every 3/4 inch. The cores are 2.4-inch OD ferrite toroids with a permeability of 250. The connectors are on the low-impedance sides. For ease of connection, the dual-core version has one winding clockwise and the other, counterclockwise. Also, in the dual-core case, the spacing between the two cores (which isn't critical) can be as small as 1/4 inch.

These transformers can also be wound with ordinary No. 14 (solid) house wire. The several samples I

tried yielded characteristic impedances close to 100 ohms (and, thus, were acceptable). The major difference lies in the voltage-breakdown capability. Units wound with Teflon-sleeved No. 14 H Thermaleze wire have been reported to withstand 10,000 volts without breakdown! Obviously, this is beyond the capability of ordinary house-wire.

Photo 8-F shows a Guanella (current) 4:1 Balun mounted in a 5 inch long by 4 inch wide by 3 inch high CU 3005-A minibox. It has 14 bifilar turns of No. 14 H Thermaleze wire on each of the two 2.4-inch OD ferrite toroids with permeabilities of 250. Each wire is covered with Teflon tubing, resulting in a characteristic impedance close to 100 ohms (the optimum). The windings also employ a crossover after the seventh turn, as shown in **Figure 8-6**. For ease of con-

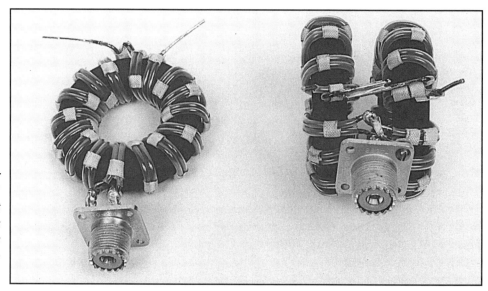

Photo 8-E. *Two high-power versions of the Guanella 4:1 Balun. The Balun on the left uses a single core while the one on the right uses two cores. The connectors are on the low-impedance sides.*

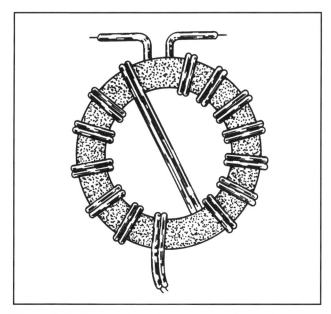

Figure 8-6. *Construction of a crossover placing input and output connections on opposite sides of the toroid.*

nection, one toroid is wound clockwise and the other, counterclockwise. The spacing between the toroids can be between 1/4 and 1/2 inch.

When matching 50-ohm cable to a balanced load of 200 ohms, the transformation ratio is constant (within 2 percent) from 1.5 to 45 MHz. This Balun can also handle the legal limit of amateur radio power. It would probably perform satisfactorily if wound with ordinary No. 14 house wire (solid), or with Teflon-covered No. 14 tinned wire. However, the design in **Photo 8-F** has withstood peak pulses of 10,000 volts! Considering this fact, it might be worthwhile to take the extra effort and use Teflon-covered No. 14 H Thermaleze wire.

A single-core version using two coiled transmission lines on a single core looks interesting and should be investigated. It results in balanced currents and unbalanced voltages. I would use two coiled transmission lines with 7 bifilar turns of the same wire on the same core as above.

Photo 8-G shows two low-power Guanella 4:1 Baluns designed to match 50-ohm coaxial cable to loads of 200 ohms. They both use No. 20 hook-up wire (solid) giving a characteristic impedance very close to the objective of 100 ohms. Their responses are flat from 1.5 MHz to well beyond 50 MHz. They are conservatively rated at 150 watts of continuous power and 300 watts of peak power. They have been exposed to 500 watts of continuous power (in a

matched condition) for a considerable length of time with virtually no rise in temperature.

The single-core version (on the left) has 7 bifilar turns on each of its two transmission lines, while the dual-core version (on the right) has 14 turns on each core. The wires are clamped together about every 1/2 inch with strips of Scotch No. 27 glass tape. The cores are 1.25-inch OD ferrite toroids with a permeability of 250. The connectors are on the low-impedance sides. As above, the dual-core version has one winding clockwise and the other, counterclockwise.

Photo 8-H is a step-down version of the Guanella 4:1 Balun and uses two ferrite rod-cores 3/8 inch in diameter and 3.5 inches in length. Core permeabilities are 125. It uses the schematic of **Figure 8-1A,** but with the generator (which is grounded) on the right side and the load (ungrounded) on the left side. This 4:1 Balun is designed to match 50-ohm coaxial cable (on the right side) to a balanced load of 12.5 ohms. Each rod has 13.5 bifilar turns of No. 14 H Thermaleze wire. Again, for ease of connection, one rod is wound clockwise and the other, counterclockwise. The response is flat from 1.5 MHz to well over 30 MHz. This Balun is fully capable of handling the legal limit of amateur radio power. The connector is on the high-impedance (50 ohms) side. Beaded versions of Guanella's step-down 4:1 Balun also look very promising for operations on the VHF and UHF bands. The technique requires minimizing the parasitics in the interconnections. Some examples will be shown later.

Photo 8-F. *A 4:1 Guanella Balun using the crossover connection of Figure 8-6 and mounted in a 5 inch long by 4 inch wide by 3 inch high CU 3005-A minibox.*

Photo 8-G. *Two low-power versions of the Guanella 4:1 Balun. The Balun on the left uses a single core while the one on the right uses two cores. The connectors are on the low-impedance sides.*

Photo 8-H. *A dual rod-core 4:1 Guanella step-down Balun designed to match 50-ohm cable to a balanced load of 12.5 ohms. The connector is on the 50-ohm unbalanced side.*

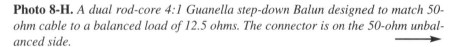

It should be mentioned again that the three dual-core Baluns above also make excellent broadband Ununs. They only sacrifice a little in low-frequency response. However, because of their conservative designs, they can still handle the 160-meter band.

Sec 8.5   Comparisons with Other Baluns

After completing the study on 4:1 Baluns, I thought it would be interesting to characterize other Baluns that are commercially available, or that have been recently described in the amateur radio literature. My findings are as follows.

The 4:1 Rod-type Ruthroff Balun

Photo 8-I shows a photograph of the typical rod-type 4:1 Balun, which was practically the only one available for the past three to four decades. The Balun in the photograph is the **HI-Q Balun.** It is the Ruthroff design (now called a *voltage* Balun[6]) with 10 bifilar turns of No. 14 wire on a 1/2-inch diameter ferrite rod 2 inches in length. In terminating this Balun with 200 ohms, the useful range was found to be from 7 to 15 MHz. Below 7 MHz, the input impedance showed a considerable inductive component—indicat-

ing autotransformer action and flux in the core (which could be harmful). Above 15 MHz, the transformation ratio increased and became complex. The optimum impedance level was found when matching 100 ohms to 25 ohms (indicating a characteristic impedance of the windings of only 50 ohms). The useful frequency range at this impedance level increased to 3.5 MHz to 30 MHz.

When matching 50-ohm coaxial cable to a 20-meter folded dipole at a height of 0.17 wavelengths (resulting in a resonant input impedance of 200 ohms), the VSWR curve was indistinguishable from that of the best Guanella 4:1 (current) Baluns.[6] This Balun also presented no difficulty in handling the full power limit. However, on 10 meters, the difference due to a very low characteristic impedance of the coiled transmission line became evident. **Figure 8-7** shows the poor VSWR curve of the rod-type Balun when compared to other Guanella and Ruthroff Baluns with characteristic impedances close to the optimum value of 100 ohms. The rod-type Balun with all of its inadequacies, which include voltage-breakdown, is certainly *not* recommended.

The high-power Ruthroff Balun is close to McCoy's design.[17] It uses 11 bifilar turns of No. 14 H Thermaleze wire on a stack of three T200-2 cores. The wires

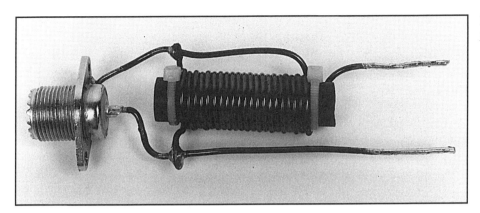

Photo 8-I. *A typical 4:1 rod-type Ruthroff (voltage) Balun (HI-Q).*

are also covered with 20-mil wall Teflon tubing yielding a characteristic impedance close to 100 ohms. I differ with McCoy's design because I feel the characteristic impedance of his transmission line could be closer to 50 ohms. His Balun and others that use powdered-iron cores will be described further in the next chapter on Baluns for antenna tuners.

The low-power units in **Figure 8-7** used 14 bifilar turns of No. 18 hook-up wire on 1.25-inch OD ferrite toroids with a permeability of 250. The transmission lines of the low-power Baluns were just under 20 inches, while those of the high-power Balun were 50 inches in length.

As can be seen in **Figure 8-7**, there are **very** small differences between the VSWR curves of the two low-power Baluns and the high-power Ruthroff

(voltage) Balun. The differences could very well be attributed to the small variations in the characteristic impedances of the windings. Very likely, the most important information gleaned from **Figure 8-7** is that, when feeding a balanced dipole with a virtual ground-plane bisecting it, the Ruthroff Balun takes on the character of a two-core Guanella Balun. In other words, the Ruthroff Balun loses its built-in high-frequency cut-off!

4:1 Current Baluns

I also characterized several so-called *current* Baluns[6] that recently appeared on the market. These are my findings:

a) They are the dual-core (toroids) version of the Guanella Balun, which sums voltages of equal delays.

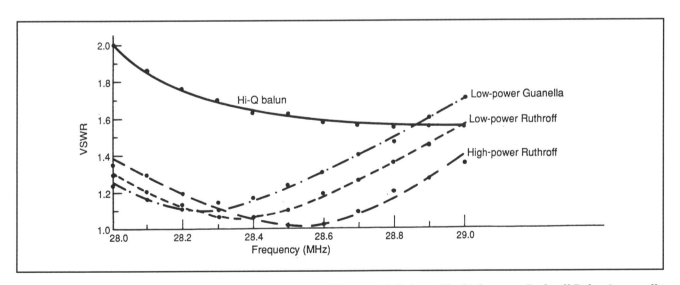

Figure 8-7. *Plots of VSWR curves on 10 meters for four different 4:1 Baluns. The high-power Ruthroff Balun is actually McCoy's design with a 100-ohm characteristic impedance winding (and is described in the next chapter). The Hi-Q Balun is shown in Photo 8-I. The comparisons show the importance of having the optimum value of the characteristic impedance of the windings and that the high-power Balun with its much longer transmission line indicates a Guanella-type operation.*

b) The electrical performances of these Baluns are vastly superior to the rod-type Balun described earlier.

c) These Baluns should meet their electrical and power-rating specifications.

d) My only criticism is that they could have more of a safety margin at the low-frequency end, where excessive core flux (due to higher than expected impedances) could take place. More inductance in the windings is recommended.

The Beaded-coax 4:1 Balun

A design in an amateur radio journal[5] advocated using beaded coaxial cable (of 100 ohms) in a 4:1 Guanella design. Various claims were advanced for this approach. I constructed one of these Baluns using No.14 wire with Teflon sleeving, resulting in the required 100-ohm characteristic impedance. Here are my findings:

a) The Balun had excellent margins at both the high- and low-frequency ends. The performance of this Balun verified the analysis (expressed earlier) with the high- and low-frequency models and the subsequent voltage gradients. In fact, the high-frequency performance exceeded the capability of my simple test equipment.[2]

b) The major disadvantage is in efficiency. Because high-permeability (2500) beads are required in order to obtain the required choking reactance in the HF band, this Balun had considerably more loss than coiled-type Baluns using low-permeability (less than 300) ferrite toroids.[2] A soak-test[2] (transformers connected back-to-back and about 500 watts applied into a dummy load) with the dual-core low-power unit in **Photo 8-G** showed that the smaller Balun ran considerably cooler! The beaded transmission line technique is recommended mainly for Baluns (and Ununs) operating at low impedance levels or on the higher-frequency bands.

Sec 8.6   Summary

Unlike the 1:1 Balun, the 4:1 Balun matching 50 ohms unbalanced to 200 ohms balanced has had no real standard for comparison in the amateur radio literature. As **Chapter 7** showed, Reisert's Balun in his 1978 article[7] had all of the attributes of a good 1:1 design. Therefore, he set a legitimate standard for others to follow or even attempt to exceed. Also

shown were some of my variations in his design for increased efficiency and ease of construction.

However, **Chapter 8** has illustrated that the designs in the amateur literature (particularly the handbooks) are found lacking in bandwidth, or efficiency, or both. Even the 4:1 Baluns on the commercial market can be improved. This is *especially* true of the rod-type Balun that has been available for decades!

In the process of investigating the 4:1 Balun for my series of articles in *CQ* and *Communications Quarterly*, I have arrived at some designs that could provide the beginnings of standards for this device. They are included in this chapter and are:

1. For *balanced* applications like matching 50-ohm cable to the 200-ohm balanced input impedance of folded-dipole or log-periodic antennas, I recommend the single-core, Ruthroff design of **Photo 8-A**. It is capable of handling the full legal limit of amateur radio power. For a higher-power capability and a little less bandwidth, I recommend the Ruthroff design shown in **Photo 8-C**. These designs are presently called *voltage* Baluns.[6]

2. For unbalanced applications like the OCFD (off-center-fed dipole), or a dipole that could be unbalanced by surrounding structures or by construction errors, I recommend the two-core Guanella design of **Photo 8-E** or **Photo 8-F**. It is a much more flexible unit that can operate successfully as a Balun when the load is grounded at its center (**Figure 8-1A**), or as an Unun when the load is grounded at the bottom. Although not shown, it can even be grounded at the top, yielding a 4:1 phase-inverter.

3. For low-power 4:1 Baluns, there really have been no designs in the literature for comparisons. Therefore, by default, the designs in this chapter are suggested as standards. Applications of the single-core Ruthroff Balun and the two-core Guanella Balun are the same as their higher-power counterparts.

I am sure there are some who don't agree with the recommendations proposed above. The Guanella (current) Balun appears to be the main Balun of choice. The question is: Why use a two-core Guanella (current) Balun when a single-core Ruthroff (voltage) Balun will do? They both have the same power ratings! For those who disagree with my views, designs, or recommendations, I encourage them to (as the classic TV commercial used to say) *put it in writing*. Then we will all benefit from the new information.

Chapter 9

Baluns for Antenna Tuners

Sec 9.1 Introduction

The 4:1 Balun, matching 50 ohms (unbalanced) to 200 ohms (balanced), has found its most popular use in antenna tuners. Because the Balun rarely sees a resistive load of 200 ohms in this application, the primary objective is to take the balanced impedance (with respect to ground) of the input to an open-wire (or twin-lead) feedline and transform it into an unbalanced impedance which has one side grounded and can be transformed into 50 ohms by an L-C matching network. This was well described in two *CQ* articles by McCoy.[17,18]

As **Chapter 8** has shown, there are two different forms of the 4:1 Balun. One uses two transmission lines wound on separate cores (or threaded through ferrite beads in some cases) and connected in parallel at the 50-ohm side and in series at the 200-ohm side. This design was first presented by Guanella in 1944,[3] and is presently called a *current* Balun.[6] The other design, using a single transmission line wound around a core and connected in a phase-inverter configuration, was introduced by Ruthroff in 1959.[9] This design, which has recently been called a *voltage* Balun,[6] is now perceived as the inferior design.

This chapter presents another view of the 4:1 Balun. It not only includes the optimum design considerations for antenna tuner use, but also the design parameters for multiband antenna systems using center-fed dipoles with open-wire or twin-lead feedlines.

Also included are my views on the G5RV antenna, the tuner using a 1:1 Balun before the L-C matching network, and the special cases of Ruthroff's 4:1 design matching into a load that is actually or virtually grounded at its center.

Sec 9.2 The Two Forms of Antenna Tuners

Three of the more common items in amateur radio jargon are VSWR, antenna tuners, and multiband antennas (especially the G5RV). These have appeared upon the scene because of the ease at which bands can now be changed and the narrow limits in the range of matching impedances with modern rigs.

The concept of using a wire antenna on many different bands isn't new. Designs have been around for more than six decades. In fact, satisfactory circuits have also been available which couple transmitters to balanced lines that present loads different than the transmitter output impedance. These were known as series and parallel-tuned circuits.[19] The transforming of a balanced impedance to an unbalanced impedance was accomplished by the isolation provided by magnetic coupling. Energy was transmitted from one circuit to the other by either having two coils in close proximity or by "link" coupling. However, these methods of coupling have fallen by the wayside, together with rock-bound rigs, plug-in coils, separate

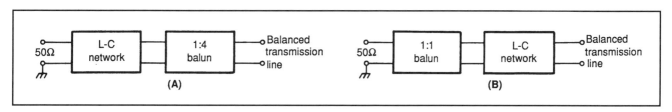

Figure 9-1. *The two basic forms of the Transmatch (antenna tuner): (A) the more popular design using an unbalanced L-C network and a 1:4 Balun; (B) a 1:1 Balun and a balanced L-C network.*

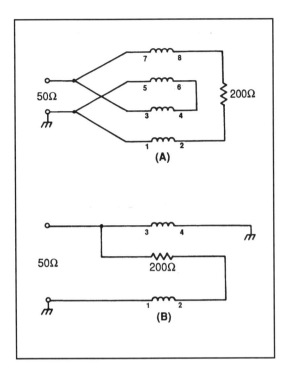

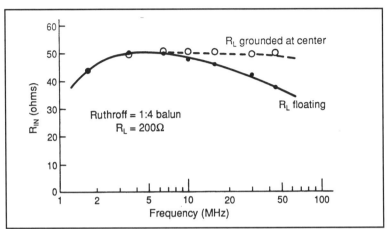

Figure 9-2. *The two basic forms of the 1:4 Balun: (A) the Guanella (current) Balun; (B) the Ruthroff (voltage) Balun.*

Figure 9-3. *The frequency response of a 4:1 Ruthroff (voltage) Balun with the load floating and with its center grounded. In the grounded case, the high-frequency response is similar to that of a 4:1 Guanella (current) Balun.*

receivers and transmitters, and (sad to say) the exciting flashing of mercury-vapor rectifiers.

Today, the *transmatch* is most often used to convert the reactive/resistive load presented by an antenna system to a nonreactive, grounded 50-ohm load. The transmatch is also commonly known as an antenna tuner. The isolation role, that of converting a balanced impedance to an unbalanced one, is now provided by the Balun transformer.

There are two basic forms of the transmatch, and they are shown in **Figure 9-1**. **Figure 9-1A**, which shows a 4:1 Balun between the L-C network and the balanced transmission line, has been the most popular. In some designs, a 1:1 Balun has been used. In either case, this form of antenna tuner places the burden on the Balun, not on the L-C network. Depending upon the dimensions of the antenna and open-wire (or twin-lead) transmission line, the Balun can see very high impedances that may be harmful. In turn, the L-C networks are simple because of their unbalanced nature. Among the most popular networks are L, pi, T, Ultimate, and SPC types.[20–23] An added advantage to this approach is that the Balun can be placed outside the operating area and connected to the L-C network by a coaxial cable.[17,18]

On the other hand, **Figure 9-1B** takes the complexity out of the Balun and places it on the L-C network. With a balanced network, the 1:1 Balun should see a lower voltage drop along the length of its transmission line (and, hence, less loss[2]) because its load is always close to 50 ohms. Additionally, the choking requirements of a 1:1 Balun are considerably less than that of the 4:1 Balun in **Figure 9-1A**.

Roehm has addressed the problems related to this form of transmatch in an article.[16] In fact, he suggests a design using an unbalanced T network and a 1:1 beaded-coax Balun. Although a balanced L-C network is inherently more complex and costly, it would be interesting to see its comparison with Roehm's unbalanced design. Additionally, a comparison with a 1:1 Balun using 50-ohm twin-lead or coaxial cable wound around a ferrite toroid with a permeability of less than 300 would also be useful. Because the 1:1 beaded-coax (choke-type) Balun requires ferrite beads with permeabilities considerably greater than 300, it has more loss.[2]

In any event, the basic form of the transmatch using the design in **Figure 9-1B** looks promising and merits further investigation.

Sec 9.3   Another View of the 4:1 Balun

This section presents my views and the results of my work on a 4:1 Balun designed for use in the very popular "antenna tuner" shown in **Figure 9-1A**. Because the Balun may be exposed to harmful high voltage conditions in this application, the efficiency and

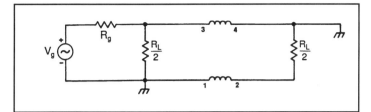

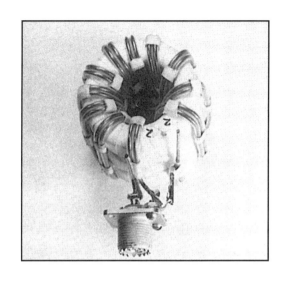

Figure 9-4. *Suggested model of the 4:1 Ruthroff (voltage) Balun when the load, R_L, is grounded at its center.*

Photo 9-A. *The high-power Ruthroff 4:1 Balun used in the comparison with other Baluns (see Figure 9-7, and Figure 8-7 of Chapter 8). Except for some difference in the characteristic impedance of the bifilar winding, it is essentially the McCoy 4:1 Balun.*

ruggedness of the core materials are important considerations. Experiments have shown that losses in Baluns are related to the impedance level[2] (and, hence, voltage level), and the permeability of the materials. Therefore, the losses are of a dielectric-type and not of a current-type, as in conventional transformers. Moreover, it is well known that powdered-iron is a more rugged and linear material than ferrite. A very important question to ask is which form of the 4:1 Balun should be used in this application—Guanella's or Ruthroff's? My conclusions may surprise many readers.

As was mentioned at the beginning of this chapter and above, there are two basic forms of the 4:1 Balun. They are shown in **Figure 9-2A** and **B**. **Figure 9-2A** is Guanella's approach. It uses two coiled transmission lines (on separate cores) connected in parallel on the 50-ohm side and in series on the 200-ohm side. This has recently been called a *current* Balun.[6] In order to have "flat" transmission lines and obtain the highest frequency response, the characteristic impedance of the coiled transmission lines should be equal to the loads they see—namely, $1/2R_L$ and, in this case, 100 ohms.

As Guanella said in his classic paper,[3] this Balun is literally "frequency independent." At the low frequency end, the reactance of the coiled transmission line should be much greater than 100 ohms (in this case) in order to assure that the energy is transmitted from input to output by an efficient transmission line mode. Beaded transmission lines aren't recommended for use on the HF band at these impedance levels because of excessive dielectric loss.

Figure 9-2B shows Ruthroff's approach, which uses a single transmission line connected in the phase-

inverter configuration (see **Chapter 7**). By grounding terminal 4, a voltage drop of $-V_1$ appears across the length of the transmission line. As a result, terminal 3 is at $+V_1$ and terminal 2 is at $-V_1$—a 4:1 transformation ratio.

It is when the load is actually grounded at its center that we see a very interesting feature of this approach. A simple impedance measurement will show that the high frequency response is *vastly* improved and that the Ruthroff (voltage) Balun appears to take on the character of a Guanella (current) Balun! **Figure 9-3** illustrates the measurements of the input impedance of a Ruthroff 4:1 Balun with the load floating, and when it is grounded at its center. These measurements (with a simple resistive bridge) were made on my design using a powdered-iron core, which will be described later.

A model for the Ruthroff 4:1 Balun, when the load is grounded at its center, is provided in **Figure 9-4**. If the characteristic impedance of the transmission line in the 4:1 Balun is 100 ohms (the optimum value if the load is 200 ohms), then the generator sees $R_L/2$ in parallel with a $R_L/2$ from a "flat" line. As a result, the generator sees its match of 50 ohms—even though the currents in the loads are not in phase!

However, when the Balun is connected to a center-fed, folded dipole, or log-periodic beam antenna with 200-ohm input impedances, the virtual ground-plane bisecting the antennas presents an interesting case. Because there is no metallic connection to the center of the load, the currents in both halves of the antennas are in phase. This is unlike the situation in **Figure 9-4**, where the current in the load on the right is delayed compared to the current in the load on the left. As is evident in **Figure 8-7** of **Chapter 8**, the VSWR curve

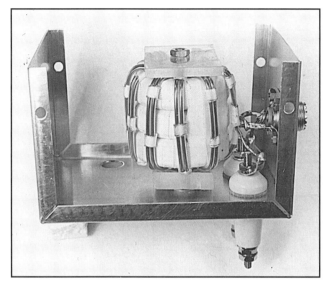

Photo 9-B. *The Balun of Photo 9-A mounted in a 5 inch long by 4 inch wide by 3 inch high minibox.*

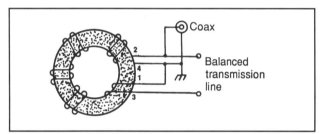

Figure 9-5. *A pictorial of the connections for a 4:1 Ruthroff (voltage) Balun.*

for the high-power Ruthroff Balun has practically the same shape as those of the two lower-power units—even though its transmission line is more than two and one half times longer.

Because the high-frequency response of a Ruthroff 4:1 Balun with a floating load is highly dependent upon the length of the transmission line, **Figure 8-7** suggests that, in the virtual ground case, the Balun acts as a Guanella Balun which sums voltages of equal phases. It also suggests that the effective electrical length of the transmission line is one-half of its actual length. I am quite sure that this model of Ruthroff's Balun was not proposed by him or by others that followed. However, it should be remembered that this condition only exists in the *balanced* case. With an unbalanced load, the Balun should introduce a reactive component that will limit the high frequency response. In the unbalanced case, the Guanella Balun with two cores is the Balun of choice.

Sec 9.4   Some "Hardy" 4:1 Designs

Photos 9-A and **9-B** show two views of a Ruthroff 4:1 Balun, much like McCoy's design, which has been used in his highly popular transmatch.[22] **Figure 9-5** shows a pictorial representation of the connections. It has 11 bifilar turns of No. 14 H Thermaleze wire on three (stacked) T200-2 cores. The cores are powdered-iron material with a permeability of 10. The OD

Photo 9-C. *The various Baluns used in the study of 4:1 Baluns for antenna tuners.*

is 2 inches. The wires are also covered with a 15-mil wall Teflon tubing, yielding a characteristic impedance close to the optimum value of 100 ohms.

I differ with McCoy's design here, because the characteristic impedance of his Balun could be closer to 50 ohms. **Photo 9-B** shows the Balun mounted in a 5 inch long by 4 inch wide by 3 inch high minibox. Because McCoy didn't use a thickly insulated wire, he wound a layer of Scotch No. 27 glass tape on each toroid before stacking. This was followed by another layer in the stacking process. With Teflon sleeving over the wire, the extra insulation provided by the glass tape could be dispensed with.

In order to improve the low-frequency response of McCoy's Balun, I made a study of higher permeability powdered-iron cores. **Photo 9-C** shows the various Baluns used in the study. The object of this study was to determine the best core material for a 4:1 Balun to be used in antenna tuners where they can be exposed to high impedances (and, hence, hostile environments). I knew, as the result of very accurate insertion loss measurements[2] that loss with ferrite materials was related to the voltage drop along the length of the transmission line and to the value of the permeability. Permeabilities of 40 (No. 67 ferrite) exhibited the lowest loss. The results taken on a single powdered-iron material—No. 2 material with a permeability of 10—also showed the very same low loss. Because powdered-iron material has been known to be more rugged and linear than ferrite material, this suggested that other powdered-irons with greater permeabilities should also be investigated.

I investigated four other powdered-irons with permeabilities of 20, 25, 35, and 75. Their designations were Nos. 1, 15, 3, and 26, respectively. Comparisons were made on input impedances (with the outputs terminated in 200 ohms) and temperature rises (when handling 500 watts of power). The power test showed, convincingly, that No. 26 material was not to be used because it showed a definite rise in temperature while the other three didn't. However, all four materials showed a definite lower input impedance than the No. 2 material, which has a permeability of 10. As expected, the higher the permeability, the larger the difference with No. 2 material. Although an input impedance measurement does provide some indication of loss because it appears as a shunting path to ground, a very accurate insertion loss measurement would provide a more precise indication of the trade-off that can be made in efficiency for low frequency response.

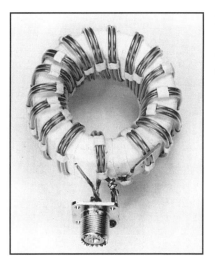

Photo 9-D. *An improved 4:1 Ruthroff design for antenna tuners.*

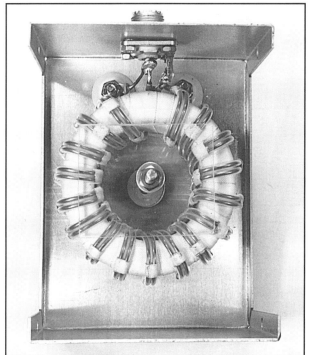

Photo 9-E. *The improved 4:1 Ruthroff Balun mounted in a 5 inch long by 4 inch wide by 3 inch high minibox.*

Because my simple loss measurements indicated that the higher permeability powdered-irons had more loss than the No. 2 material, I decided to design a 4:1 Ruthroff Balun using this material—but with a larger core and more turns than the McCoy[17,18] Balun. Although McCoy's design has enjoyed considerable success over the years, I felt that a larger inductive reactance was desirable in order to assure better performance on the lower frequency bands (particularly 160 meters).

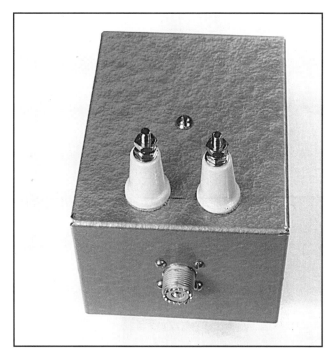

Photo 9-F. *The top view of the 4:1 Balun of Photo 9-E.*

The specific design is shown in **Photo 9-D**. It has 17 bifilar turns of No. 14 H Thermaleze wire on a T300A-2 powdered-iron core, which has an OD of 3 inches and a permeability of 10. With this number of turns and a larger cross section than the three T200-2 cores, the low frequency response improved by a factor of about two over the McCoy Balun, which has 10 to 12 turns on a stack of three T200-2 cores. Furthermore, the wires are also covered with 15-mil wall Teflon tubing, resulting in a characteristic imped-

ance of 100 ohms (the objective). This well-insulated transmission line has been reported to handle 10,000 volts without breakdown. **Figure 9-3** illustrates the performance of this Balun (under a matched condition) when the load is floating and when it is center-tapped-to-ground. **Photo 9-E** shows the Balun mounted in a minibox 5 inches long by 4 inches wide by 3 inches high. **Photo 9-F** shows the top view of the mounted Balun.

Because the Balun with the larger core and more turns showed an improvement by a factor of two in the low-frequency response over the McCoy Balun, I constructed an even larger design. This is shown in **Photo 9-G**. It has 21 turns of the same wire on a T400A-2 core with an OD of 4 inches and a permeability of 10. Even though **Photo 9-G** shows the toroid wrapped with Scotch No. 27 glass tape, as mentioned earlier, this extra insulation isn't required because the wires are covered with Teflon sleeving.

Figure 9-6 shows the comparisons in the input impedances versus frequency of these three "hardy" Baluns when they are terminated in 200-ohm loads grounded at their centers. As can be seen, the low-frequency response of the Balun with the most turns and largest core is the best. Even though the Balun with the 3-inch core has a poorer low-frequency response, it is an improvement over the McCoy Balun and should find considerable use in transmatches. **Figure 9-6** also shows that the high frequency responses of these Baluns with the loads grounded at their centers are remarkably similar. This is especially interesting, as the length of the transmission line on the larger

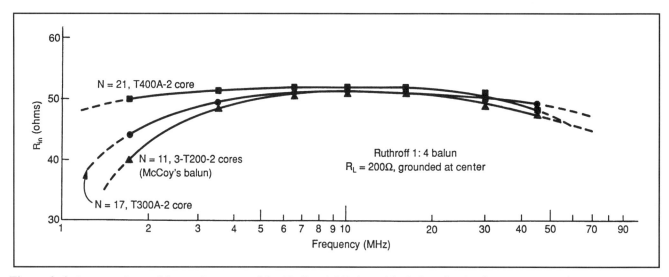

Figure 9-6. *A comparison of the performance of the McCoy 4:1 Balun with Baluns having larger cores and more turns.*

Balun (with the T400A-2 core) is more than twice as long as the other two (115 inches compared to 50 and 55 inches). If it is correct that my model of a Ruthroff (voltage) Balun feeding a balanced antenna or transmission line takes on the character of a Guanella (current) Balun because of the virtual ground, then this large Balun could have many applications.

Sec 9.5   Multiband Dipoles

Antenna tuners have been known to work well for some radio amateurs and not for others. This is due to the differences in the dimensions of their antenna systems. With high impedances seen by the 4:1 Baluns in the antenna tuners, the Baluns not only fail to provide a good balanced-to-unbalanced conversion, but they can also be damaged by excessive heating. The high current, low impedance condition seen by the Balun isn't a problem. Therefore, the object in multiband antenna design is to provide the most favorable impedances for the Baluns, especially on the three lowest frequency bands—40, 80, and 160 meters. Usually on the higher frequency bands, the impedances seen by the Baluns are not as high and the Balun's choking reactances are greater (assuring balanced-to-unbalanced conversion). This section discusses three cases of multiband center-fed dipole designs. They are 1) the "worst case" design, 2) a smaller design—the G5RV, and 3) a larger design. Others may have better designs for multiband operation, but it's clear that the "worst case" design ought to be avoided. **Figure 9-7** shows the symbols for the dimensions of the center-fed dipoles.

Sec 9.5.1   The "Worst Case" Design

Apparently, an 80-meter dipole with a quarter-wave open-wire (or twin-lead) feedline is a logical design for a multiband dipole. In **Figure 9-7** this would mean that $L_1 = L_2 = 59$ to 67 feet, depending upon the favorite operating frequency. If one were to use 450-ohm twin-lead with "open windows," L_2 would be diminished by 10 percent; with 300-ohm TV twin-lead, it would be diminished by about 20 percent. This would make a good antenna system on 160 meters. Because $L_1 + L_2$ is close to a quarter-wave, the current at the input to the feedline is at its highest value and the impedance at its lowest—a very favorable condition for the Balun. In fact, a 1:1 Balun at the feedpoint would probably do a good job.

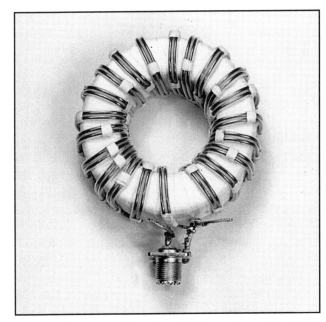

Photo 9-G. *A large 4:1 Ruthroff design using a 4-inch OD powdered-iron core and 21 bifilar turns.*

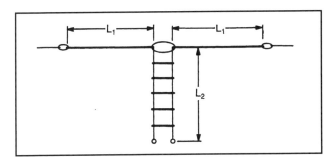

Figure 9-7. *The symbols used for the dimensions of a center-fed dipole with open-wire feeders (or twin-lead with appropriate consideration of velocity factors).*

However, what does the input to the feedline look like on 80 meters? If 450-ohm feedline is used, the 4:1 Balun sees a quarter-wave 450-ohm feedline terminated in approximately 50 ohms. Transmission line theory tells us that the Balun would see 4050 ohms—an impossible condition for most Baluns. The situation becomes worse on 40 meters, where we may have a center-fed, full-wave dipole with a half-wave transmission line (a 1:1 matching transformer). In this case, the Balun could see an impedance approaching 10,000 ohms—a more than impossible condition! Although high impedances would also be seen on 10, 15, and 20 meters, the conditions are not quite as severe because the Balun's choking reactances are usually greater and the impedances lower. In essence, the "worst case" design for a 4:1 Balun is the "best case" design (except for 160 meters), if one still uses inductive coupling to a parallel-tuned circuit.[19]

Sec 9.5.2 A Smaller Design— The G5RV

Varney,[24] G5RV, designed a multiband center-fed antenna system capable of operation on all HF bands from 3.5 to 30 MHz. In contrast to multiband antennas designed as half-wave dipoles on 80 meters (the "worst case" design), the full-size G5RV antenna was designed as a three-half-wave antenna on 14,150 MHz with a 1:1 transmission line matching transformer. It was possible to accomplish this using the dimensions of 51 feet for L_1 and 34 feet for L_2. For 450-ohm twin-lead with "windows," L_2 would be 31 feet; for 300-ohm TV ribbon, L_2 would be 28 feet. Consequently, the input impedance at the base of the matching transmission line was about 100 ohms on 14,150 MHz, and a manageable impedance for 50 or 80-ohm coaxial cable.

However, with a total length for $L_1 + L_2$ of 85 feet, the impedances at the input to the transmission line on 40, 80, and 160 meters are also manageable. Even though they have a reactive component on these bands, they aren't so high that a well-designed 4:1 Balun in an antenna tuner can't handle them easily. Varney also showed that the highest impedances occurred on the 18-, 21-, and 28-MHz bands. However, this doesn't present a problem with the design shown in **Photo 9-D** because it uses an efficient core material, and it also has the highest reactances of its windings at these frequencies.

Varney[24] also wrote, at considerable length, on the unsuitability of a Balun being used to connect the base of the 34-foot open feeders to a coaxial cable feedline. He stated that if a Balun is connected to a reactive load with a VSWR of more than 2:1, its internal losses would increase. Varney also mentioned heating of the wires and saturation of the core. Evidently Varney was not familiar with McCoy's design, which uses a powdered-iron core (with a permeability of 10) that can withstand VSWRs considerably greater than 2:1—without showing any temperature rise. Furthermore, the wire doesn't heat up; however, the core itself does via dielectric heating. Additionally, with sufficient choking reactance, Baluns can handle (equally) the resistive and reactive components of an impedance.

Finally, after observing the voltage and current distributions on all of the bands, it appears that a 2:1 (100:50-ohm) Balun might be an interesting one to try on the G5RV antenna. It could be that many of the bands would not require the added matching of an antenna tuner. If some of the bands require an antenna tuner in order to be used, then I would suggest using a "hardened" Balun. That is what I call McCoy's approach, which uses efficient and hardy powdered-iron cores. A 2:1 Balun, comprised of a 1:2 Unun in series with a 1:1 Guanella (current) Balun, could be easily designed and built (see **Chapter 10**).

Sec 9.5.3 A Larger Design

Even though the G5RV antenna can be made to operate on 160 meters with a suitable antenna tuner, an antenna system larger than the "worst case" design can provide better operation on the 40-, 80-, and 160-meter bands. As you might expect, an antenna system about twice as large as the G5RV offers these advantages. Suggested dimensions are $L_1 = 80$ feet and $L_2 = 100$ feet. If the feedline is 450-ohm twin-line with "windows," then $L_2 = 90$ feet. If it is 300-ohm TV ribbon, then $L_2 = 82$ feet. As with the G5RV, it's the total length of $L_1 + L_2$ that presents favorable or unfavorable impedances to the 4:1 Balun in the antenna tuner. Therefore, L_1 and L_2 could both be 90 feet, as well. Only very small differences in performance would be noticed between these two systems, particularly on the lower-frequency bands. Obviously, other combinations totaling 180 feet are also possible. In the G5RV case, it's 85 feet.

Sec 9.6 Summary

After reading this chapter, one might think that I have set this technology back a few years by advocating voltage Baluns and powdered-iron cores. I have even questioned the professional literature. However, my conclusions were based upon three experimental results. These were: 1) measurements with my resistive bridge on input impedances of 4:1 Ruthroff (voltage) Baluns with loads floating and center-tapped-to-ground, 2) VSWR measurements on folded dipoles with various 4:1 Baluns (large and small and, therefore, with many different lengths of transmission lines), and 3) McCoy's success with his 4:1 Balun. Also, as this chapter points out, it helps to have the dimensions of a multiband, center-fed dipole, and feeders favor the operation of a 4:1 Balun in antenna tuners. And, *yes*, there is a "worst case" antenna design!

As in many investigations, supplying answers to some questions can lead to others that appear to be important. Specifically, for powdered-irons, how would permeabilities in the 20 to 35 range perform? Simple impedance measurements showing lower values on input impedances, indicate that there is more loss than with a permeability of 10; but accurate insertion loss measurements are needed in order to tell the complete story—the trade-off in efficiency for low-frequency response.

Finally, low permeability ferrite-like No. 67 material with a permeability of 40 looks interesting for use in Baluns for antenna tuners. Accurate insertion loss measurements[2] have also shown the very same high efficiency that was exhibited by powdered-iron having a permeability of 10. With a sufficient number of turns on an appropriate size core, a Balun made of this material could be practical. Even though the amateur radio literature still refers to the problem of core saturation, there has been only one recorded case. This was on 2 MHz with a rod-type 1:1 Balun where insufficient choking reactance exists.[13,14]

Chapter **10**

1.5:1 and 2:1 Baluns

Sec 10.1 Introduction

There are many applications for broadband Baluns with impedance transformation ratios close to 1.5:1 and 2:1. Two applications involve matching 50-ohm cable to balanced loads of 75 or 100 ohms, which are the input impedances of a half-wave dipole at heights of 0.22 or 0.34 wavelengths above ground. Another, is the matching of 50-ohm cable to the 100-ohm input impedance of a quad antenna. An interesting, and somewhat unexpected, application is the matching of 50-ohm cable directly to the input impedance of the driven element of a Yagi beam antenna of 33 or 25 ohms. This would eliminate the common hairpin matching network presently used to raise their input impedances to 50 ohms.

There are many versions of these two Baluns. They include: 1) high- and low-power designs, 2) designs matching 50-ohm cable to higher or lower impedances, 3) series- or parallel-type designs, 4) single- or dual-core designs, 5) dual-ratio designs, and 6) HF and VHF designs. The series-type Baluns use an Unun (unbalanced-to-unbalanced transformer) in

series with a Guanella (current) Balun. More details on these Ununs are provided in later chapters. In this chapter, you'll read about many high-power designs capable of handling the full legal limit of amateur radio power. They are optimized for sufficient margins in choking reactance at their low frequency ends, and in efficiency throughout their passbands. Two of the 2:1 Baluns are specifically designed for 2-meter operation.

Sec 10.2 1.5:1 Baluns

In this section, I'll present two series-type 1.5:1 Baluns (actually 1.56:1, which should be close enough). They both use 1.56:1 Ununs in series with Guanella 1:1 Baluns. **Figures 10-1A** and **B** show their schematic diagrams. **Figure 10-1B** has an extra input (to a tap), which provides another ratio of 1.33:1.

The left-hand side of **Photo 10-A** shows a design using **Figure 10-1A** mounted in a CU 3006 minibox 5.25 inches long by 3 inches wide by 2.25 inches high (RadioShack has carried a similar enclosure). The 1:1.56 Unun has 4 quintufilar turns on a 1.5-inch OD

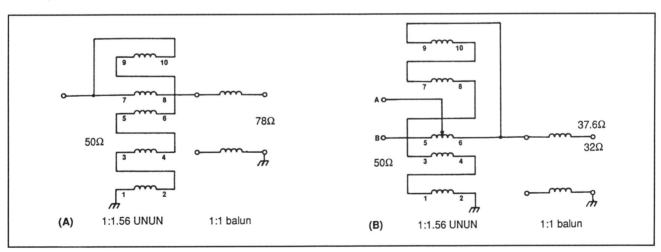

Figure 10-1. *Schematic diagrams of two 1.56:1 Baluns: (A) step-up, 50:78 ohms; (B) step-down, 50:37.6 ohms—connection A, 50:32 ohms—connection B.*

65

Photo 10-A. *Baluns using the schematic diagrams of Figure 10-1. Balun on the left matches 50-ohm cable to a balanced load of 78 ohms. Balun on the right matches 50-ohm cable to balanced loads of 37.6 or 32 ohms.*

ferrite toroid with a permeability of 250. Winding 7-8 is No. 14 H Thermaleze wire and the other four are No. 16 H Thermaleze wire.

The 1:1 Guanella Balun has 11 bifilar turns of No. 14 H Thermaleze wire on a 2.4-inch OD ferrite toroid with a permeability of 250. One wire is covered with Teflon tubing, resulting in a characteristic impedance very close to 78 ohms (the optimum value).

When matching 50-ohm cable to a balanced load of 78 ohms, the impedance transformation ratio is literally flat (within a percent or two) from 1.5 MHz to 40 MHz! You might be interested to know that (separately) the 1:1 (75:75-ohm) Balun would make an excellent isolation transformer for 75-ohm hardline, and the 1.56:1 (78:50-ohm) Unun an excellent match between 75-ohm hardline and 50-ohm cable.

The right-hand side of **Photo 10-A** shows a design using **Figure 10-1B** mounted in a similar enclosure. The 1.56:1 Unun has 5 quintufilar turns on a 1.5-inch OD ferrite toroid with a permeability of 250. Winding 5-6 is No. 14 H Thermaleze wire and is tapped at one turn from terminal 5. The other four wires are No. 16 H Thermaleze.

The 1:1 Guanella Balun has 7 turns of homemade coaxial cable on a 1.5-inch OD ferrite toroid with a permeability of 250. The inner conductor is No. 14 H Thermaleze wire and is covered with Teflon tubing. The outer braid, which is from a small coaxial cable or from 1/8-inch tubular braid, is also tightly wrapped with Scotch No. 92 tape to preserve the low characteristic impedance.

In matching 50-ohm cable to a balanced load of 37.6 ohms (connection A), or to a balanced load of 32 ohms (connection B), the response is essentially flat (within a percent or two) from 1.5 to 30 MHz.

Sec 10.3   2:1 Baluns

The 2:1 Balun lends itself to more choices in design than the 1.56:1 Balun. This is especially true because the parallel-type design, which provides a 2.25:1 Balun with the widest possible bandwidth, can easily be employed. The 1.56:1 Balun is at a disadvantage here. This section presents many Baluns using both series and parallel-type designs.

Sec 10.3.1   Series-type Baluns

Figure 10-2 shows circuit diagrams for two versions of the series-type Balun. **Photo 10-B** shows a design using **Figure 10-2A** mounted in a CU 3005-A minibox 5 inches long by 4 inches wide by 3 inches high. The 1:2 Unun has 7 trifilar turns on a 1.5-inch OD ferrite toroid with a permeability of 250. The output tap is located 6 turns from terminal 5. Winding 5-6 is No. 14 H Thermaleze wire and the other two are No. 16 H Thermaleze wire.

The 1:1 Guanella Balun has 14 bifilar turns of No. 14 H Thermaleze wire on a 2.4-inch OD ferrite toroid with a permeability of 250. Both wires are covered with Teflon tubing, which results in a characteristic impedance of 100 ohms (the optimum value). A crossover, placing 7 turns on one side of the toroid

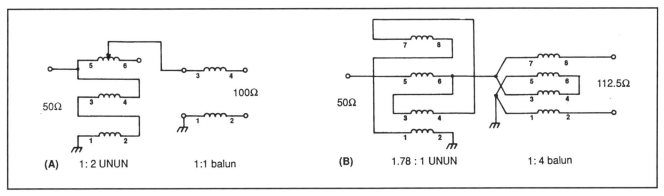

Figure 10-2. *Schematic diagrams of two versions of the series-type Balun: (A) 1:2 (50:100 ohms) Balun; (B) 1:2.25 (50:112.5 ohms) Balun.*

and 7 turns on the other, is used so the output and input are on opposite sides of the toroid. **Figure 10-3** is a drawing of the crossover. Although this technique has no electrical advantage at HF, the mechanical advantage is obvious.

When matching 50-ohm cable to a balanced load of 100 ohms, the response is literally flat (within 2 to 3 percent) from 1.5 to 30 MHz. By connecting the output of the Unun to terminal 6 instead of to the tap, the Balun would match 50-ohm cable to a balanced load of 112.5 ohms with about the same response.

Photo 10-C shows two slightly different versions of series-type 2.25:1 Baluns using the circuit of **Figure 10-2B**. Both have the same 1.78:1 step-down Unun, which has 5 quadrifilar turns on a 1.5-inch OD ferrite toroid with a permeability of 250. Winding 5-6 is No. 14 H Thermaleze wire, and the other three are No. 16 H Thermaleze wire. Each version also has 8 bifilar turns of No. 14 H Thermaleze wire on both of the 1.5-inch OD ferrite toroids, with a permeability of 250.

The differences are: 1) the Balun on the left in **Photo 10-C** has one layer of Scotch No. 92 tape on one of the wires in each bifilar winding and a crossover after the fourth turn, and 2) the Balun on the right has two layers of Scotch No. 92 tape on one of the wires on one toroid and no extra insulation on the wires of the other toroid. Therefore, one of the windings in the 1:4 Guanella Balun has a characteristic impedance a little less than 50 ohms and the other a little greater than 50 ohms, resulting in a canceling effect. Furthermore, the crossover isn't used in this design. The Balun on the left is mounted in a CU 3006 minibox 5.25 inches long by 3 inches wide by 2.25 inches high. The Balun on the right is mounted in a CU 3015-A minibox 4 inches long by 2 inches wide by 2.75 inches high.

Photo 10-B. *A series-type Balun using the schematic diagram of Figure 10-2A designed to match 50-ohm cable to a balanced load of 100 ohms.*

The performance of these two Baluns is essentially the same. When matching 50-ohm cable to balanced loads of 112.5 ohms, the responses are essentially flat (within 2 to 3 percent) from 1.5 to 30 MHz.

From preliminary measurements on series-type 2:1 Baluns, the Balun in **Photo 10-B** is the one I'd recommend for matching 50-ohm cable to balanced loads of 100 ohms, while the Baluns in **Photo 10-C** would be best for matching to balanced loads of 112.5 ohms. Also, by replacing the 1.78:1 Unun in **Figure 10-2B** with a 2.25:1 Unun, and not adding any extra insulation to the windings of the 1:4 Balun, it's possible to obtain an excellent Balun matching 50-ohm cable to a balanced load of 89 ohms.

Figure 10-4 shows the schematic diagram of a series-type Balun designed to match 50-ohm cable to balanced loads of 25 or 22.22 ohms. **Photo 10-D**

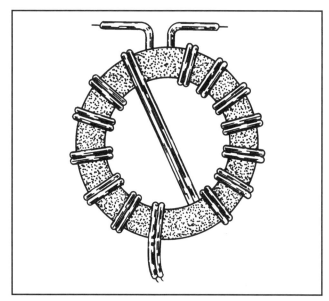

Figure 10-3. *Construction of a 1:1 Guanella Balun with a crossover placing the input and output terminals on opposite sides of the toroid.*

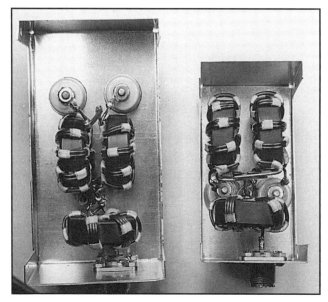

Photo 10-C. *Two series-type Baluns using the schematic diagram of Figure 10-2B designed to match 50-ohm cable to balanced loads of 112.5 ohms.*

shows two versions of this dual-ratio Balun. The Balun on the left, for its Unun, has 6 trifilar turns of No. 14 H Thermaleze wire on a 1.5-inch OD ferrite toroid with a permeability of 250. Winding 3-4 is tapped one turn from terminal 3, yielding the 2:1 ratio. The 1:1 Guanella Balun has 6 turns of homemade coaxial cable on a similar toroid. The inner conductor is No. 12 H Thermaleze wire and is covered

with Teflon tubing. The outer braid, from a small coax or from 1/8-inch tubular braid, is tightly wrapped with Scotch No. 92 tape to preserve its low characteristic impedance.

In matching 50-ohm cable to balanced loads of 25 ohms (connection A) or to 22.22 ohms (connection B), the response is essentially flat (within a percent or two) from 1.5 to 30 MHz.

The Balun on the right in **Photo 10-D** has similar windings on a single 2.4-inch OD ferrite toroid with a permeability of 250. Its performance is quite comparable to the Balun on the left.

Sec 10.3.2 Parallel-type Baluns

As you saw in the previous section, the series-type Baluns presented here are combinations of Ununs with ratios of 1.33:1, 1.78:1, 2:1, and 2.25:1 in series with Guanella 1:1 or 4:1 Baluns. The Ununs, which are really an extension of Ruthroff's[9] bootstrap technique for obtaining a 4:1 Unun, sum direct voltages with delayed voltages that traverse a single transmission line. Therefore, the Unun eventually limits the high-frequency response of the series-type Balun.

On the other hand, the parallel-type Balun is an extension of Guanella's technique of summing voltages of equal delays. Instead of simply connecting transmission lines in parallel-series, the parallel-type Balun connects Guanella Baluns in parallel-series. As I noted in **Reference 25**, two 4:1 Guanella Baluns can be connected in parallel-series, yielding very broadband ratios of 6.25:1. This section shows how a 1:1 Guanella Balun can be connected with a 4:1 Guanella Balun in parallel-series, yielding a very broadband ratio of 2.25:1.

Figure 10-5 is the schematic diagram of the high-frequency model of a 2.25:1 Unun which is used for analysis purposes. Because the current through the load is $3/2I_1$, the transformation ratio is $(3/2)^2$, or 2.25:1. Therefore, if the impedance seen on the left side is 50 ohms, a matched impedance on the right side is 22.22 ohms. Because two thirds of the 50 ohms appears across the input of the Guanella 1:1 Balun, its optimum characteristic impedance is 33.33 ohms. Similarly, this is also the value of the optimum characteristic impedance for the windings of the 4:1 Balun. Because the 1:1 Balun wants to see 33.33 ohms on its output (a matched condition) and the 4:1 Balun wants to see 66.66 ohms, placing these two values in parallel results in the confirming value of 22.22 ohms.

If the 50-ohm generator is placed on the right side in **Figure 10-5**, the circuit becomes a step-up Unun matching 50 ohms to 112.5 ohms (on the left). If the ground is removed on the left side, the transformer becomes a Balun. A similar analysis as above, shows that the optimum characteristic impedance of the three bifilar windings now becomes 75 ohms.

Photo 10-E shows a parallel-type 2.25:1 Balun designed to match 50-ohm cable to a balanced load of 112.5 ohms. It has 9 bifilar turns of No. 14 H Thermaleze wire on each of the three toroids that have a 1.5-inch OD and a permeability of 250. Also, one of the wires on each toroid is covered with Teflon tubing, resulting in a characteristic impedance of 75 ohms (the optimum value). When operating as a Balun, the response is essentially flat from 7 MHz to over 45 MHz. As an Unun, the flat response is broadened from 1.5 MHz to over 45 MHz.

Because the coiled wire, parallel-type Balun didn't provide any real advantage over the series-type Balun (in fact, the low-frequency response was poorer), I investigated the beaded transmission line version for possible use in the VHF band. **Figure 10-6** shows a schematic diagram of one using coaxial cable. Obviously, twin lead could be substituted for the coaxial cable. **Photo 10-F** shows both versions.

The top design in **Photo 10-F** has 4 inches of 3/8-inch OD ferrite beads with a permeability of 125 on each of the three 75-ohm transmission lines. It is designed to match 50-ohm cable on the right to a bal-

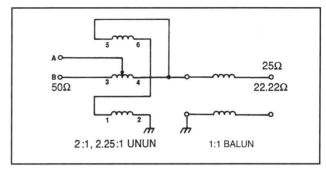

Figure 10-4. *Schematic diagram of a dual-ratio series-type Balun. Connection A matches 50-ohm cable to a balanced load of 25 ohms. Connection B matches 50-ohm cable to a balanced load of 22.22 ohms.*

anced load of 112.5 ohms on the left (with the ground on terminal 1 removed). The transmission lines consist of two No. 14 H Thermaleze wires separated by the Teflon tubing covering one of them. When matching 50-ohm cable to a balanced load of 112.5 ohms, the response is essentially flat from 30 MHz to over 100 MHz (the limit of my bridge).

The bottom design in **Photo 10-F** also has 4 inches of 3/8-inch OD ferrite beads with a permeability of 250. However, they are now threaded by homemade coaxial cable with a characteristic impedance of 33.33 ohms. It is designed to match 50-ohm cable on the left to a balanced load of 22.22 ohms (with the ground on terminal 2 removed). The inner conductor of the coax is No. 14 H Thermaleze wire and is covered with

Photo 10-D. *Two series-type Baluns using the schematic diagram of Figure 10-4 designed to match 50-ohm cable to balanced loads of 25 ohms or 22.22 ohms.*

Photo 10-E. *Parallel-type 2.25:1 Balun matching 50-ohm cable to a balanced load of 112.5 ohms.*

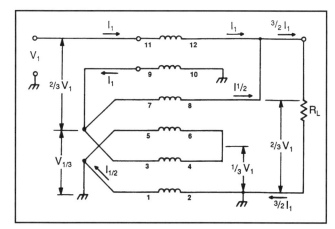

Figure 10-5. *High-frequency model of the parallel-type 2.25:1 transformer. Connections shown are for Unun operation.*

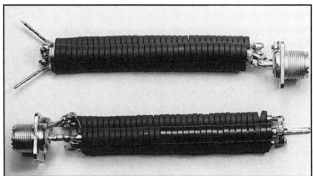

Photo 10-F. *Beaded transmission line versions of the 2.25:1 parallel-type Balun for operation in the VHF band. The top Balun matches 50-ohm cable to a balanced load of 112.5 ohms. The bottom Balun matches it to a balanced load of 22.22 ohms.*

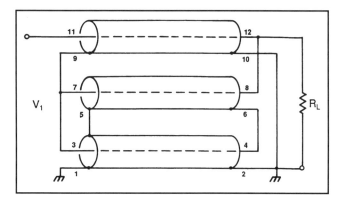

Figure 10-6. *The coaxial cable version of the parallel-type 2.25:1 transformer of Figure 10-5.*

Teflon tubing. The braid is from small coaxial cable or from 1/8-inch tubular braid. The braid is also tightly wrapped with Scotch No. 92 tape in order to preserve the low characteristic impedance. When matching 50-ohm cable to a balanced load of 22.22 ohms, the response is essentially flat from 14 MHz to over 100 MHz (again, the limit of my bridge).

Sec 10.4   Closing Comments

In closing, I'd like to make a couple of comments regarding parallel-type Baluns.

First, if you are interested in a 1.78:1 ratio, replace the 1:4 Balun in **Figures 10-5** and **10-6** with a 1:9 Guanella Balun (three transmission lines connected in parallel-series). This would yield an output current of $4/3I_1$ and a ratio of $(4/3)^2$, or 1.78:1. If you replace the 1:4 Balun with a 1:16 Guanella Balun (four transmission lines connected in parallel-series), the output current will be $5/4I_1$, with a ratio of $(5/4)^2$, or 1.56:1.

Second, because the parallel-type Balun is really an extension of Guanella's technique of summing voltages of equal delays,[26,27] the high-frequency response is mainly limited by the parasitics in the interconnections. Therefore, beaded transmission lines offer the best opportunity for successful operation on the VHF band. It is also recommended that the ferrite beads have permeabilities of 300 or less[2] in order to achieve the very high efficiencies of which these transformers are capable.

Chapter 11

6:1, 9:1, and 12:1 Baluns

Sec 11.1 Introduction

This chapter is a combination of two articles I wrote for *Communications Quarterly*. One, on the 6:1 and 9:1 Baluns, appeared in the Winter 1993 issue and the other, on the 12:1 Balun, ran in the Summer 1993 issue. I combined these two articles here because the three Baluns discussed have much in common. Commonalities include: 1) They are the most difficult to construct and are, therefore, the most expensive; 2) two of them, the 6:1 and 12:1 Baluns, use Ununs in series with Guanella Baluns; 3) two of them use the 9:1 Guanella Balun—the 12:1 Balun with a series 1.33:1 Unun; 4) they are generally associated with two-wire transmission lines with characteristic impedances of 300, 450, and 600 ohms, respectively; 5) when matching 50-ohm cable to higher impedances, they have more loss than the Baluns in the preceding chapters; and 6) the optimum application of these Baluns requires a more critical understanding of the trade-offs in low-frequency response for efficiency.

Like the 2:1 Balun in **Chapter 10**, the 6:1 (actually 6.25:1) Balun also comes in two forms: the series-type, which offers better low-frequency response in the HF band, and the parallel-type, which has a vastly greater high-frequency capability. The parallel-type 6:1 Balun, together with the 9:1 Guanella Balun (which is also a parallel-type), offer the potential for designs capable of efficient and broadband operation on the VHF and UHF bands.

Sec 11.2 6:1 and 9:1 Baluns

Many radio amateurs associate the use of the 6:1 and 9:1 Baluns with 300-ohm twin lead feeding folded dipoles, 450-ohm "ladder" line feeding single or multi-band antenna systems. However, what is neglected (in some cases) is the effect of the height of these antennas above earth and the length of the transmission lines feeding them.

Broadband 6:1 and 9:1 Baluns are considerably more difficult to construct than the more common 1:1 and 4:1 Baluns. This is especially true when matching 50-ohm cable to impedances of 300 and 450 ohms. Furthermore, there are some important trade-offs in low-frequency response for efficiency.

From what I could gather "on the air" or talking to radio clubs, I have determined what I believe are probably two of the most common misconceptions regarding the use of these Baluns:

1. 6:1 Baluns. In free-space, the folded dipole with 300-ohm twin-lead has a resonant impedance close to 300 ohms. The dipole also has this value at a height of about 0.225 wavelength above ground. However, it's only 200 ohms at a height of about 0.17 wavelength and 400 ohms (the maximum) and at 0.35 wavelength. In many cases, the 4:1 Balun would actually do a better job of matching.

2. 9:1 Baluns. Some are unaware of the relationship between the impedance at the input of a transmission line, the characteristic impedance of the line, and the impedance at the end of the line. Just because a transmission line has a characteristic impedance of 450 ohms doesn't necessarily mean that a 9:1 Balun will perform a satisfactory match to 50-ohm cable. Far from it. For example, if the line is terminated by a half-wave dipole with an impedance of 50 ohms, the 9:1 Balun would see 50 ohms when the line is a half-wave long and 4050 ohms when it's a quarter-wave long! Broadband Baluns cannot be designed to handle impedances as high as 4050 ohms. It's very likely that a well-designed 50:450-ohm Balun would experience (particularly on 80 and 160 meters) harmful flux in the core *and* excessive heating because of the large voltage drop along the length of its transmission lines. This problem of presenting very high (and harmful) impedances to Baluns is quite prevalent with multi-band antenna systems.

Clearly, there are many applications for 6:1 and 9:1 Baluns. They not only include matching 50-ohm cable

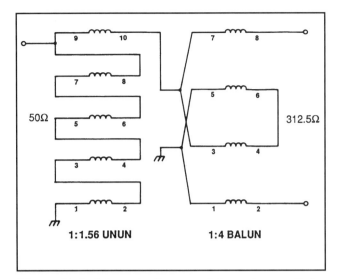

Figure 11-1. *Schematic diagram of the series-type Balun with a 1:6.25 ratio designed to match 50 to 312.5 ohms.*

to balanced loads of 300 and 450 ohms, but also to balanced loads of 8 and 5.6 ohms, as well. Furthermore, many of the designs in this chapter will perform almost as well in Unun (unbalanced-to-unbalanced) applications. The trade-off (which is usually very small) is in low-frequency response. Additionally, these Baluns could be used to exploit the low-loss properties of 300- and 450-ohm twin-lead where very long transmission lines are used. This is especially important at 14 MHz and above.

In the pages that follow, I'll present a variety of Baluns matching 50-ohm cable to 300 ohms (actually to 312.5 ohms, a 6.25:1 ratio) and to 450 ohms, as well as 50-ohm cable to 8 and 5.6 ohms. Also included are two different versions of 6.25:1 Baluns. One is a series-type using a 1.56:1 Unun in series with a 4:1 Guanella Balun and the other a series-parallel

arrangement using two 4:1 Guanella Baluns. Because the series-parallel Balun adds voltages of equal delays, you'll find its high-frequency capability is much greater.

The 9:1 Balun is a conventional Guanella Balun with three transmission lines connected in series at the high-impedance side and in parallel at the low-impedance side. Therefore, it also sums voltages of equal delays. Some of the comparisons and analyses of these 6.25:1 and 9:1 Baluns were probably published for the first time in my Winter 1993 *Communications Quarterly* article.

Sec 11.2.1 6.25:1 Series-Type Baluns

Figure 11-1 shows the schematic diagram of a series-type Balun designed to match 50-ohm cable to a balanced load of 312.5 ohms. It consists of a 1:1.56 Unun in series with a 1:4 Guanella Balun. The overall ratio of 1:6.25 should satisfy most of the 1:6 requirements. **Photo 11-A** shows three examples. All three Baluns use the same step-up Unun that has four quintufilar turns on a 1.5-inch OD ferrite toroid with a permeability of 250. Winding 9-10 is No. 14 H Thermaleze wire and the other four are No. 16 H Thermaleze wire. Because this Unun sums only one delayed voltage with four equal direct voltages, it has an excellent high-frequency response.[2]

The Balun on the left in **Photo 11-A** has eight bifilar turns of No. 18 hook-up wire on each transmission line of its 1:4 Balun. The wires are further spaced with No. 18 Teflon tubing providing a characteristic impedance close to 150 ohms (the optimum value). The ferrite toroid has a 2.4-inch OD and a permeability of 250. When matching 50-ohm cable to a floating

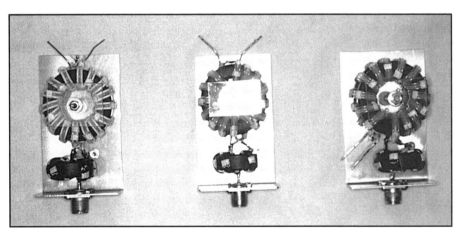

Photo 11-A. *Three examples of series-type 1:6.25 Baluns. The Balun on the right, with a double-core 1:4 Balun, has both a balanced voltage and current output. The other two only have balanced-current outputs.*

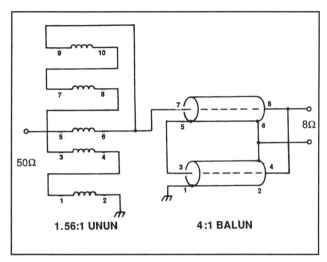

Figure 11-2. *Schematic diagram of the series-type Balun with a 6.25:1 ratio designed to match 50 to 8 ohms.*

load of 312.5 ohms, the response is essentially flat from 1.7 to 30 MHz. Under matched conditions, 500 watts of continuous power and 1 kW of peak power is a conservative power rating. Because the 1:4 Balun in this series-type 1:6.25 Balun uses only one core instead of two, this transformer should never be used when the load is grounded at its center. Also, it is not recommended for balanced antennas. This series-type Balun presents balanced currents, but does *not* present balanced voltages.

The Balun in the center of **Photo 11-A** has seven bifilar turns of No. 16 SF Formvar wire on each transmission line on its 1:4 Balun. The wires are covered with Telfon sleeving and further separated by No. 16 Teflon tubing. Like the Balun on the left, the characteristic impedance is also close to the objective of 150 ohms. The toroid also has a 2.4-inch OD and a permeability of 250. When matching 50-ohm cable to a floating load of 312.5 ohms, the response is essentially flat from 3.5 to 30 MHz. Over this frequency range, this Balun can easily handle the full legal limit of amateur radio power. Because this Balun also presents balanced currents and not balanced voltages, it should not be used when the loads are balanced to ground or grounded at their centers.

The Balun on the right in **Photo 11-A** has 14 bifilar turns of No. 16 SF Formvar wire on each of the two toroids of the 1:4 Balun. The wires are also covered with Teflon sleeving and further separated by No. 16 Teflon tubing. For ease of connection, one core is wound clockwise and the other counterclockwise. The two cores are spaced 1/4 inch apart with acrylic

sections. When matching 50-ohm cable to a 312.5 load that is either floating, balanced to ground, grounded at its center, or grounded at its bottom (a broadband Unun), the response is essentially flat from 1.7 to 30 MHz. Under this matched condition, it can easily handle the full legal limit of amateur radio power. Furthermore, this is a true Balun because it presents equal currents and equal voltages. If one were to measure the voltages-to-ground, when matching into a balanced load, one would find them to be equal and opposite. The other two 1:6.25 Baluns using single-core 1:4 Baluns, would have equal currents but not equal voltages (see **Chapter 8**). Because they are easier to construct, it would be interesting to compare them with a true Balun.

Figure 11-2 shows the schematic diagram of a series-type Balun designed to match 50-ohm cable to a balanced load of 8 ohms (perhaps a short-boom Yagi). It consists of a 1.56:1 step-down Unun in series with a Guanella 4:1 step-down Balun. The overall ratio is 6.25:1. **Photo 11-B** shows two examples. Both Baluns use the same step-down Unun, which has four quintufilar turns on a 1.5-inch OD ferrite toroid with a permeability of 250. Winding 5-6 is No. 14 H Thermaleze wire and the other four are No. 16 H Thermaleze wire. The interleaving of the wires is such that the performance is optimized for matching 50 to 32 ohms.

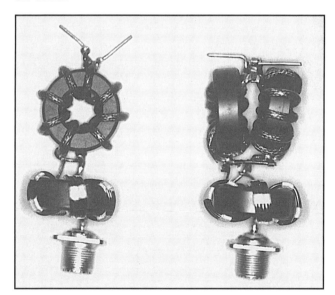

Photo 11-B. *Two examples of the series-type 6.25:1 Balun optimized at the 50:8-ohm level. The Balun on the left is designed to match into a floating 8-ohm load. The Balun on the right is designed to match into an 8-ohm floating, center-tapped-to-ground or grounded load (Unun).*

The Balun on the left in **Photo 11-B** has four turns of low-impedance coaxial cable on each transmission line on the single-core 4:1 Balun. The inner conductor is No. 14 H Thermaleze wire, and it has two layers of Scotch No. 92 polyimide tape. The outer braid is from a small coax (or 1/8-inch tubular braid) and is tightly wrapped with Scotch No. 92 tape to achieve the 17-ohm characteristic impedance (the optimum value). The ferrite toroid has a 1.5-inch OD and a permeability of 250. When matching 50-ohm cable to a floating load of 8 ohms, the response is flat from 1 to 40 MHz. In a matched condition, this Balun can easily handle the full legal limit of amateur radio power.

The Balun on the right in **Photo 11-B** has six turns of the same coaxial cable on each of the two cores of the Guanella step-down Balun. The cores also have a 1.5-inch OD and a permeability of 250. The performance of this Balun is practically the same as the above with the single-core 4:1 Balun. The important differences are that this 6.25:1 Balun also performs equally well whether the load is center-tapped-to-ground, balanced-to-ground, or grounded at the bottom (a broadband Unun). This is the one recommended for feeding a short-spaced Yagi beam antenna.

Sec 11.2.2   6.25:1 Parallel-Type Baluns

The 6.25:1 series-type Baluns described in the preceding section consisted of a 1.56:1 Unun, which is an extension of Ruthroff's bootstrap approach for Ununs,[9] in series with a Guanella 4:1 Balun.[2] The

upper-frequency limit for this combination is really set by the Unun, which sums a delayed voltage with four direct voltages. The parallel-type 6.25:1 Baluns described in this section are really extensions of Guanella's approach, which sums voltages of equal delays. Therefore, the upper-frequency limit is mainly dependent upon the parasitics in the interconnections.

The 6.25:1 parallel-type Balun uses two 4:1 Guanella Baluns connected in parallel on the low-impedance side and in series on the high-impedance side. As you will see, one of the Baluns is reversed, giving the desired ratio of 6.25:1. Other combinations can produce different fractional-ratios (other than $1:n^2$ where n is 1, 2, 3, . . .), like 2.25:1 and 1.78:1. Because very little practical design information is available regarding this family of very broadband Baluns,[26,27] this section also includes my high-frequency analysis of the 6.25:1 parallel-type Balun. It should also be pointed out that very little sacrifice in performance occurs whether the load is grounded at its center or at the bottom (as an Unun).

Figure 11-3 shows the coiled-wire version of the 6.25:1 parallel-type Balun. For analysis purposes, the voltages and currents are also shown. As can be seen, the top 4:1 Balun is connected as a step-down Balun, while the bottom 4:1 Balun is connected as a step-up Balun. The Baluns are in series on the high-impedance side (on the left) and in parallel on the low-impedance side (on the right). As **Figure 11-3** illustrates, the lower 1:4 Balun adds a current of $0.5I_1$ to the load, resulting in a total current of $2.5I_1$. Thus, the impedance transformation ratio is 2.5^2, or 6.25:1.

For maximum high-frequency response, each transmission line should see a load equal to its characteristic impedance. In other words, they should be "flat" lines. If the high side on the left is 50 ohms, then 40 ohms appears on the input of the top Balun and 10 ohms on the input of the bottom Balun. Consequently, the optimum characteristic impedance for *all* transmission lines is 20 ohms. On the low-impedance side on the right, the top Balun wants to see 10 ohms, while the bottom Balun wants to see 40 ohms. Because 10 ohms in parallel with 40 ohms equals 8 ohms, each Balun conveniently sees its ideal load and a broadband ratio of 6.25:1 is obtained.

If the Balun is required to match 50-ohm cable (on the right side) to a balanced load of 312.5 ohms (on the left side), the same analysis shows that the optimum characteristic impedance of all the transmission lines is 125 ohms.

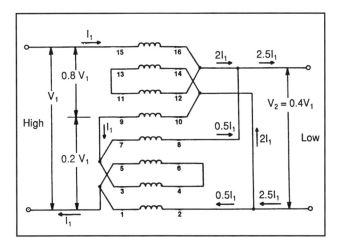

Figure 11-3. *Schematic diagram of the parallel-type Balun (and Unun) with a 6.25:1 ratio. The currents and voltages are shown for analysis purposes (see text).*

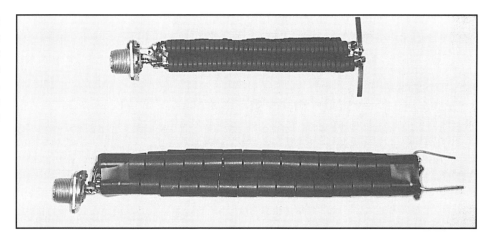

Photo 11-C. *Two beaded-line versions of the parallel-type 6.25:1 Balun (and Unun). The top transformer is designed to match 50-ohm cable to 8 ohms. The bottom transformer is designed to match 50-ohm cable to 312.5 ohms.*

Because the parallel-type Balun (or Unun) sums voltages of equal delays and, therefore, has no built-in high-frequency cut-off, it has a real advantage over the series-type Balun on the VHF bands and above. Furthermore, beaded transmission lines with low-permeability ferrite beads (125 and less) can be used, resulting in high efficiencies. On the HF band, where coiled windings are generally used, the series-type Balun is preferred because of its simplicity.

Photo 11-C shows two beaded-line 6.25:1 transformers. The top Balun, designed to match 50-ohm cable (on the left) to 8 ohms (on the right), uses low-impedance coaxial cable lines. The schematic diagram is shown in **Figure 11-4**. It has 5 inches of 0.375-inch OD beads (permeability 125) on four coaxial cables with characteristic impedances of 20 ohms. The inner-conductors of No. 12 H Thermaleze wire have two layers of Scotch No. 92 polyimide tape. The outer braids, from small coaxial cable or 1/8-inch tubular braid, are also wrapped tightly with the same tape in order to preserve the 20-ohm characteristic impedance. When matching 50 ohms to 8 ohms, the response is essentially flat from 10 MHz to beyond 100 MHz (the limit of my simple bridge). Under this matched condition, this Balun can easily handle the full legal limit of amateur radio power. Furthermore, it has practically the same performance when operating as an Unun (both terminals 1 and 2 grounded). In the Unun application, the bottom transmission line has no voltage along it and, therefore, requires no beads.

The bottom Balun in **Photo 11-C**, which is designed to match 50-ohm cable to a balanced load of 312.5 ohms, has 8 inches of 0.5-inch OD beads on 125-ohm twin-lead transmission lines. The ferrite beads also have a permeability of 125. The wires are No. 14 H Thermaleze wire and are covered with Teflon sleeving. They are further separated by No. 18

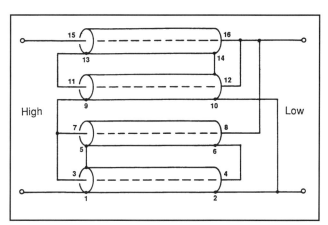

Figure 11-4. *Schematic diagram of the coaxial-cable version of the parallel-type 6.25:1 Balun (and Unun).*

Teflon tubing. When matching 50-ohm cable (on the right side) to 312.5 ohms (on the left side), the response is essentially flat from 20 MHz to over 100 MHz. Under this matched condition, this Balun can also easily handle the full legal limit of amateur radio power. Additionally, this transformer performs practically as well when used as an Unun.

Sec 11.3   9:1 Baluns

The broadband 9:1 Balun, matching 50-ohm cable to a balanced load of 450 ohms, is one of the most difficult ones to construct because high-impedance transmission lines (150 ohms) are required for maximum high-frequency response, and greater reactances are needed in order to isolate the input from the output. So one can appreciate the task at hand, this section also provides a brief review of the theory of these devices.[2]

Figure 11-5 shows the high- and low-frequency models of the Guanella 9:1 Balun that connect three transmission lines in series at the high-impedance side and in parallel at the low-impedance side. Because Guanella's Baluns (which can be easily converted to Ununs) sum voltages of equal delays, they offer the highest frequency capability.

The high-frequency model (**Figure 11-5A**) assumes there is sufficient choking reactance in the coiled (or beaded) transmission lines to isolate the input from the output and only allow transmission line currents to flow. Under this condition, the analysis is rather straightforward as it only involves transmission line theory. Simply stated—the maximum high-frequency response occurs when each transmission line is terminated in a load equal to its characteristic impedance, Z_o. Thus, the transmission lines in the 9:1 Balun have no standing waves. Because each transmission line sees one third of the load, the optimum value of Z_o is $R_L/3$. Except for parasitics in the interconnections and self-resonances in coiled windings, Guanella's approach is literally "frequency independent."

On the other hand, the low-frequency analysis of the Guanella 9:1 Balun is most important because it reveals the major difficulty in designing them for low-loss, wideband operation. **Figure 11-5B** is the model for determining the low-frequency response. It assumes that no energy is transmitted to the load by a transmission line mode. Although the terminology and analysis is the same as that used for conventional autotransformers, the similarity ends when there is sufficient choking reactance to only allow for the efficient transmission line mode.

As with conventional transformers, one can analyze the low-frequency response of the 9:1 Balun from either the low- or high-impedance side. By putting the generator on the low-impedance side in **Figure 11-5B**, I've chosen to analyze it from that side. With the output open-circuited, the generator sees four coiled (or beaded) lines connected in series-parallel. The net result is that the generator sees the reactance of only *one* coiled (or beaded) line. To prevent a shunting current to ground (and/or autotransformer operation), the reactance the generator sees should be much greater than R_g (at least by a factor of 10 at the lowest frequency of interest). The inductance of the coiled or beaded line that prevents the unwanted currents is still known as the magnetizing inductance, L_M.

What's important to note here is that the low-frequency model of the Guanella 4:1 Balun does not have the series-parallel combination of coiled or beaded lines.[2] Only two lines, which are in series, exist in its model. Therefore, for a two-core Guanella 4:1 Balun having the same number of turns (and same cores) as a 9:1 Guanella Balun, its low-frequency response is better by a factor of two!

Another advantage that goes to the Guanella 4:1 Balun when matching 50 to 200 ohms, is in the number of turns that can be wound on the same cores. Since 4:1 Baluns require characteristic impedances of 100 ohms (instead of 150), the width of the transmission lines is considerably less, thus allowing for more turns. Also, as will be shown later, the efficiency of the 4:1 Balun is greater because the potential drops

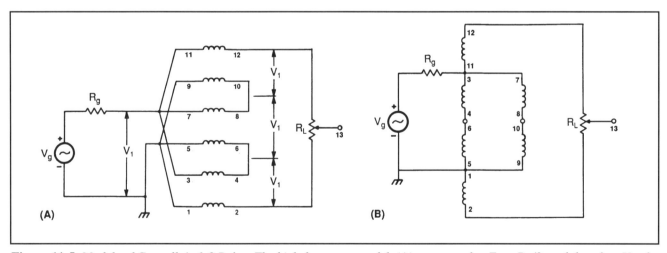

Figure 11-5. *Models of Guanella's 1:9 Balun. The high-frequency model, (A), assumes that $Z_o = R_L/3$, and therefore V_2, the output of each transmission line, equals V_1. The low-frequency model, (B), assumes no energy is transmitted to the load, R_L, by a transmission line mode.*

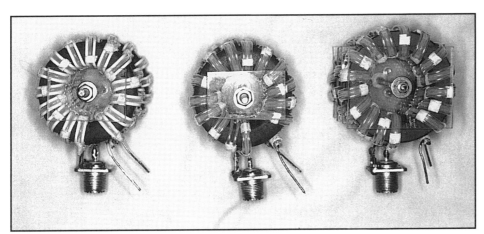

Photo 11-D. *Three broadband Guanella 9:1 Baluns designed to match 50-ohm cable to 450 ohms. The transformer on the left, using No. 18 hook-up wire, can handle 500 watts from 1.7 to 45 MHz. The transformer in the center, using No. 16 wire, can handle 1 kW from 3.5 to 45 MHz. The transformer on the right (with larger cores), using No. 16 wire, can handle 1 kW from 1.7 to 45 MHz.*

along the transmission lines are lower (less dielectric loss). Finally, as you can see from **Figure 11-5B**, by also grounding terminal 2 (Unun operation), windings 1-2 and 3-4 are both shorted—degrading the low-frequency response because L_M is reduced by one third.

Another interesting analysis with Baluns and Ununs concerns the potential gradients (voltage drops) along the transmission lines. Because the loss with these transformers, when transferring the energy via a transmission line mode, is a dielectric-type (voltage dependent), the higher the gradient, the greater the loss. The interesting cases occur when the load is: a) floating, b) grounded at the center, and c) grounded at the bottom (an Unun).

Floating load. With terminal 13 in **Figure 11-5A** ungrounded, the top transmission line has a gradient of $+V_1$ and the bottom transmission line has a gradient of $-V_1$. The center transmission line has a gradient of zero. Therefore, the center transmission line only acts as a delay line and doesn't require a magnetic core or beads. As a result, the top and bottom cores (or beads) account for the dielectric loss.

Load grounded at the center. With terminal 13 grounded at the center of the load, the top transmission line has a gradient of $+V_1$, the bottom transmission line has a gradient of $-V_1$, and the center transmission line has a gradient of $-V_1/2$. This configuration results in about 25 percent more loss because of the extra gradient along the center transmission line. Incidentally, this condition exists when matching into balanced systems like 450-ohm transmission lines or antennas because they have virtual grounds at the center of the loads they present.

Load grounded at the bottom. With terminal 13 grounded at the bottom of the load (an Unun), the top and center transmission lines have gradients of $+V_1$.

The bottom transmission line has no gradient and, therefore, no loss. It only acts as a delay line and thus requires no magnetic core or beads.

Sec 11.3.1   Some Practical 9:1 Balun Designs

Photo 11-D shows three versions of the broadband Guanella 9:1 Balun designed to match 50-ohm cable to 450-ohm loads. The transformer on the left has 15 bifilar turns of No. 18 hook-up wire on each of the three ferrite toroids with a 2.4-inch OD and permeability of 250. The wires are further separated by No. 16 Teflon tubing, resulting in a characteristic impedance close to 150 ohms (the optimum value). The cores in this Balun, as well as the other two that follow, are spaced 1/4 inch apart by sections of acrylic. In matching 50 to 450 ohms, the response is essentially flat from 1.7 to 45 MHz. In this matched condition, this transformer can easily handle 500 watts of continuous power and 1 kW of peak power.

The transformer in the center of **Photo 11-D** has 14 bifilar turns of No. 16 SF Formvar wire on each of the three ferrite toroids with a 2.4-inch OD and permeability of 250. The wires are covered with Teflon sleeving and further separated by No. 16 Teflon tubing. The characteristic impedance is also close to the optimum value of 150 ohms. In matching 50 to 450 ohms, the response is essentially flat from 3.5 to 45 MHz. In this matched condition, this transformer can easily handle 1 kW of continuous power and 2 kW of peak power. **Photo 11-E** shows this Balun mounted in a minibox 6 inches long by 5 inches wide by 4 inches high.

The transformer on the right in **Photo 11-D** is designed to handle 1 kW of continuous power and 2 kW

Photo 11-E. *The Guanella 9:1 Balun shown mounted in a large minibox.*

of peak power from 1.7 to 45 MHz. Because this transformer uses larger cores with slightly higher permeabilities (2.68-inch OD and 290 permeability), which are not as popular as those used in the other two Baluns, it is much more expensive to construct. It has 16 bifilar turns of No. 16 SF Formvar wire on each toroid. The wires are covered with No. 16 Teflon sleeving and further separated with No. 16 Teflon tubing. In matching 50 to 450 ohms, the response is flat from 1.7 to 45 MHz.

Finally, **Figure 11-6** shows the schematic diagram of a 9:1 Balun (or Unun) using coaxial cables wound around ferrite cores or threaded through ferrite beads. This form of the transformer is especially useful when matching 50-ohm cable to 5.6 ohms because the choking reactance of the magnetizing inductance, L_M, only need be much greater than 5.6 ohms. **Photo 11-F** shows two different designs.

The transformer on the top has 9 1/2 turns of low-impedance coaxial cable on each rod. The rods are 1/2 inch in diameter, 2 1/2 inches long, and have a permeability of 125. The low-frequency response of this Balun is quite insensitive to the length and permeability of the rods.[2] The inner conductors of the coaxial cables are No. 12 H Thermaleze wire with two layers of Scotch No. 92 tape. The outer braids are made from small coax (or 1/8-inch tubular braid). They are further wrapped with Scotch No. 92 tape to preserve the low-impedance of 17 ohms. In matching 50-ohm cable to 5.6 ohms, the response is essentially flat from 1.7 to 30 MHz. The optimum impedance level was

found when matching 40 to 4.45 ohms. The addition of another layer of Scotch No. 92 tape would optimize this transformer at the 50:56-ohm level, and the high-frequency response would exceed 100 MHz. This transformer is very efficient and should handle the full legal limit of amateur radio power easily.

The bottom transformer in **Photo 11-F** is designed to match 50-ohm cable to a load of 5.6 ohms in the VHF band. It uses 3 1/2 inches of beads on three low-impedance coaxial cables. The ferrite beads have an OD of 3/8 inch and a permeability of 125. The inner conductors of the coaxes are No. 12 H Thermaleze wire with one layer of Scotch No. 92 tape. The outer conductors are from small coaxes or 1/8-inch tubular braid, and are also tightly wrapped with Scotch No. 92 tape to preserve the low characteristic impedance. In matching 50-ohm cable to 5.6 ohms, the response is essentially flat from 7 MHz to over 100 MHz (the limit of my test equipment). This 9:1 Balun (which can be used as an Unun) can handle the full legal limit of amateur radio power under matched conditions, because of the low-permeability beads and the low-voltage gradients along the lengths of its transmission lines.

Sec 11.4   Concluding Remarks on 6:1 and 9:1 Baluns

One of the most important properties of broadband Baluns and Ununs (which all use ferrites) is their capability of having extremely high efficiencies. Knowing the loss mechanism in these transformers and the trade-off in low-frequency response for efficiency allows one to optimize their applications. In the paragraphs that follow, I'll discuss the losses and

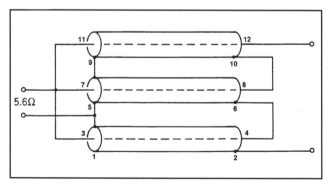

Figure 11-6. *Schematic diagram of a coaxial cable (beaded or coiled) 9:1 Guanella Balun (or Unun). This design is especially useful in matching 50-ohm cable to 5.6 ohms over a very wide bandwidth.*

trade-offs involved with the transformers presented in the preceding sections. The approach used here should be applicable to all forms of transmission line transformers. This section ends with a review of two articles that contained 9:1 Baluns. As you'll see, I have some rather different views on the claims made in these articles.

Accurate measurements on many broadband Ununs have found the losses to be related to the permeability and the impedance level.[2] Permeabilities greater than 300 resulted in excessive losses. Because these losses are unlike the conventional transformer whose losses are current-dependent, it can only be assumed that their losses are voltage dependent; in other words a dielectric-type loss. Therefore, higher-impedance transformers have higher voltage gradients along their transmission line and, thus, have greater losses. Additionally, it was found that the higher the permeability, the greater the loss with frequency. Taking into account the accurate measurements and the factors noted above, I offer these loss values for the transformers in the preceding sections:

1.56:1 Ununs. The 1.56:1 Ununs (either step-up or step-down) used in series with Guanella 4:1 Baluns to form 6.25:1 Baluns have the lowest potential gradients along their transmission lines. Voltage drops of only about 0.2 V_1, where V_1 is the input voltage, exist along their transmission lines. Accurate measurements have shown losses, in a matched condition, of only 0.04 dB. If the cores, which have a permeability of 250, were replaced with cores having a permeability of 125, the losses could be as low as 0.02 dB over much of the passband. The low-frequency response would still be acceptable at 1.7 MHz. This Unun is a natural for matching into 75-ohm hard line when long transmission lines are required.

6.25:1 and 9:1 Low-impedance Baluns. Baluns matching 50-ohm cable to 8 or 5.6 ohms, also have very low voltage drops along their transmission lines. Generally, they are about twice that of the 1.56:1 Unun. Therefore, the losses with these Baluns should be on the order of 0.1 dB in their passbands.

6.25:1 High-impedance Baluns. The losses in the series-type Baluns are mainly in the 1:4 Guanella Baluns, which have potential gradients of about 1.25 V_1, where V_1 is the input voltage. From previous measurements at this impedance level, the suggestion is that the losses (with ferrites of 250 permeability) should be about 0.1 dB at 7 MHz and 0.2 dB at 30 MHz. By using toroids with permeabilities of 125,

the losses could be 0.07 dB and 0.15 dB, respectively. However, with a permeability of 40, the losses could be as low as 0.05 dB within the passband. However, one must consider the sacrifice in low-frequency response incurred when using these lower-permeability ferrites. With a permeability of 125, it's poorer by a factor of 2. With a permeability of 40, it's poorer by a factor of 8! The 6.25:1 parallel-type Balun in this article uses ferrite beads with a permeability of 125 and, therefore, should have losses similar to its series-type counterpart.

9:1 High-impedance Baluns. As was shown in the preceding section, the potential gradient along two of the transmission lines is V_1, where V_1 is the input voltage. The third transmission line, with a balanced load (or as an Unun), has no potential gradient and, consequently, no loss in its core. Because the loss with the series-type Balun mainly exists in one core, the loss with the 1:9 Balun should be a little less than twice as great. With ferrite cores of 250 permeability, the suggested losses are 0.2 dB at 7 MHz and 0.4 dB at 30 MHz. With cores of 125 permeability, the losses are about 0.14 and 0.28 dB, respectively. Again, by using cores with permeabilities of 40, the losses are practically negligible—approximately 0.1 dB within its passband.

As in the case of the 1:6.25 Baluns above, similar trade-offs occur in the low-frequency response. That is, if 125 permeability cores are used, the low-frequency response is poorer by a factor of 2; with 40 permeability cores, it's poorer by a factor of 8. The major difference here is that the low-frequency performance of the

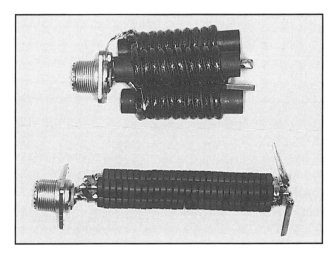

Photo 11-F. *Two versions of the coaxial-cable 9:1 Guanella Balun (or Unun) designed to match 50-ohm cable to 5.6 ohms*

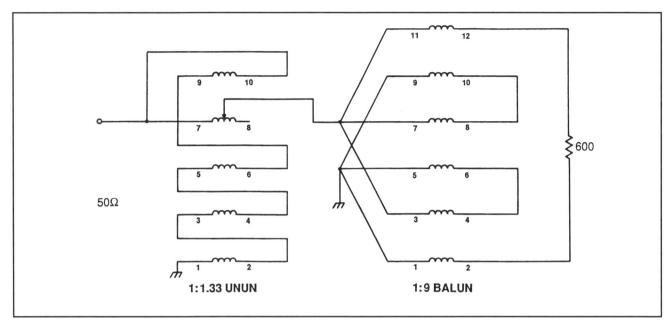

Figure 11-7. *Schematic diagram of the series-type 12:1 Balun using a 1:1.33 Unun in series with a 1:9 Guanella Balun.*

9:1 Balun, as seen by its low-frequency model, isn't as good as the 4:1 Balun that controls the low-frequency response of the series-type 1:6.25 Balun. Additionally, it should be pointed out that all of the suggested losses for the transformers in this chapter are for matched conditions—that is with VSWRs of 1:1. If the VSWR is 2:1 due to a load twice as large as the objective, the input voltage to the Balun increases by about 40 percent. Therefore, the losses should increase by close to the same percentage.

In closing this section, I would like to report my findings on two recent articles in amateur radio journals that also described 9:1 Baluns matching 50-ohm cable to 450 ohms. One[5] advocated using three 150-ohm coaxial cables threaded through high-permeability ferrite beads—a 9:1 Guanella Balun. Because of the low voltage-breakdown capability of the coaxial cable and the high loss found by accurate measurements on Ununs using these high-permeability ferrites, the design was suspect. I built a copy of the design and found it to be, as expected, unable to handle any appreciable power. The second article[28] advocated using 14 trifilar turns of "magnet wire" on a 2-inch OD powdered-iron core (permeability of 10). This Balun was also constructed and tested. Again, as was expected, when matching 50-ohm cable to a floating load of 450 ohms, the 9:1 Balun barely reached a true 9:1 ratio at 7 MHz. Above 7 MHz, the ratio became greater than 9:1 and also introduced a

reactive component. Below 7 MHz, there was insufficient choking reactance to prevent flux in the core. My three objections to this design are: 1) a trifilar design has a poor high-frequency response because it sums a direct voltage with a delayed voltage that traverses a single transmission line and a delayed voltage that traverses two transmission lines, 2) the characteristic impedances of the transmission lines are only 50 ohms (the objective is 150 ohms), and 3) the low-frequency response is poor because of the low-permeability powdered-iron core. I do not recommend either of the designs in these two articles.

Sec 11.5   12:1 Baluns

Over the years, the broadband, 12:1 Balun has been of special interest to users of rhombic and V antennas. With the aid of this Balun, certain advantages over multi-element arrays can be fully exploited. Rhombics and Vs are easier to construct, both electrically and mechanically, and there are no particularly critical dimensions or adjustments. Furthermore, they give satisfactory gain and directivity over a 2-to-1 frequency range. These antennas have also been found to be more effective in reception. Because their designs can present input impedances of 600 ohms, and very long lengths of highly efficient 600-ohm open-wire line can be used between the shack and the antenna, an efficient and broadband 12:1 Balun is a natural for

Photo 11-G. *Top view of the high-power 12:1 Balun.*

Photo 11-H. *Side view of the high-power 12:1 Balun.*

this application. However, to my knowledge, satisfactory Baluns have not been available for this use.

I will present two versions of a series-type Balun designed to match 50-ohm cable to a balanced load of 600 ohms. One is a high-power unit designed to handle the full legal limit of amateur radio power over a bandwidth of 7 to 30 MHz. The other is a medium-power unit capable of handling approximately one-half the legal limit of amateur radio power from 3.5 to 30 MHz. Both Baluns use a 1:1.33 Unun in series with a 1:9 Guanella Balun.

As you will see, these Baluns are not especially easy to design and construct. The major difficulties lie in trying to obtain sufficient choking reactances in the coiled windings to meet the low-frequency requirements, and large enough characteristic impedances of the windings to meet the high-frequency requirements. Because a coiled winding with a characteristic impedance of 200 ohms (the objective) is practically impossible to obtain with any reasonable wire size and number of turns, I used the compensating technique first described in my book.[2] Because the characteristic impedances of the 9:1 Guanella Balun are somewhat less than 200 ohms, a compensating effect (and hence higher frequency response) can be obtained by having a higher (than the normal objective) characteristic impedance of the windings in the 1:1.33 Unun. Earlier work (also described in my book) presented a 12:1 Balun using a 1:3 Unun in series with a

1:4 Ruthroff Balun. The Baluns presented in this section using a 1:1.33 Unun in series with a Guanella 1:9 Balun, are much improved designs.

Sec 11.5.1   A High-power 12:1 Balun

Figure 11-7 shows the schematic diagram of the series-type 12:1 Balun used in both the high- and medium-power versions. **Photo 11-G** shows a top view of the high-power Balun. **Photo 11-H** shows a side view.

The 1:1.33 Unun has 5 quintufilar turns on a 1.5-inch OD ferrite toroid with a permeability of 250. Winding 7-8 is No. 14 H Thermaleze wire and the other four are No. 16 H Thermaleze wire. Winding 7-8 is also tapped at 3 turns from terminal 7.

The 1:9 Guanella Balun has 8 bifilar turns of tinned No. 16 wire on each of the three toroids. Each wire is covered with Teflon tubing and further separated by two Teflon tubings. The characteristic impedance of the windings is about 190 ohms (the objective is 200 ohms). The ferrite toroids have an OD of 2.4 inches and a permeability of 250. The spacing between the toroids is 1/2 inch.

In matching 50-ohm cable to a balanced load of 600 ohms, the response is literally flat (within a percent or two) from 7 to 30 MHz. Within this bandwidth, it is capable of handling the full legal limit of amateur

Photo 11-I. *Top view of the medium-power 12:1 Balun.*

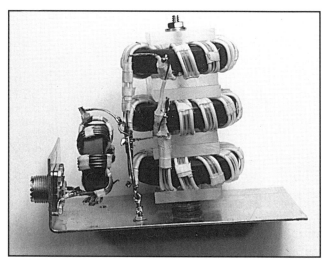

Photo 11-J. *Side view of the medium-power 12:1 Balun.*

radio power. In a matched condition, the expected insertion loss is about 0.25 dB.

Sec 11.5.2   A Medium-power 12:1 Balun

Photo 11-I shows the top view of the medium-power 12:1 series-type Balun. **Photo 11-J** shows the side view. This Balun also has the same 1:1.33 Unun as described earlier.

The 1:9 Guanella Balun has 11 bifilar turns of No. 18 hook-up wire on each toroid. The wires are further separated by two No. 18 Teflon tubings. The characteristic impedance of the windings is about 170 ohms. The toroids have an OD of 2.4 inches and a permeability of 250. The spacing between the toroids is also 1/2 inch.

In matching 50-ohm cable to a balanced load of 600 ohms, the response varies less than 5 percent from 3.5 to 30 MHz. Within this bandwidth, the Balun can handle about one-half the legal limit of amateur radio power. As with the high-power version, the expected insertion loss is also 0.25 dB.

Sec 11.6   Concluding Remarks on 12:1 Baluns

Many of the concluding remarks from the discussion on 6:1 and 9:1 Baluns (**Sec 11.4**) also apply to 12:1 Baluns; therefore, I won't repeat them here. But the following four remarks are specific to 12:1 Baluns and warrant mentioning:

First, high-impedance transmission line transformers like the 12:1 Balun are particularly sensitive to

metallic enclosures. If a minibox were to be used, I would suggest the one shown in **Photo 11-E**, which is 6 inches long by 5 inches wide by 4 inches high. Smaller metallic enclosures would reduce the characteristic impedances of the windings and affect the high-frequency response. Even the spacing between cores had to be increased from 1/4 inch (for a 50:450-ohm Balun) to 1/2 inch. The subchassis shown in the photographs were used because they provided the necessary electrical and mechanical support.

Second, the 12:1 Baluns described in this section also make excellent Ununs, albeit with some compromise in the low-frequency response. I would suggest using the high-power unit only between 14 and 30 MHz and the medium-power unit only between 7 and 30 MHz.

Third, for the readers interested in VHF operation, I would suggest the parallel-type approach described in the earlier section on 6:1 Baluns. In this case, a 9:1 Guanella Balun is connected in series-parallel with a 1:4 Guanella Balun. This would produce a broadband ratio of 12.25:1. By using 170-ohm twin-lead (about 10 inches long) threaded through ferrite beads with a permeability of 125, it appears that it is possible to match 50-ohm cable to a balanced load of 612.5 ohms throughout the VHF band.

Fourth, by using torids with a permeability of 125 in the 1:9 Guanella Baluns (of the 12:1 Baluns), the insertion loss would be reduced by around one half (0.12 dB), with a trade-off in low-frequency response. The high-power unit would now cover about 10 to 30 MHz, and the medium-power Balun would cover about 7 to 30 MHz.

Chapter 12

The 4:1 Unun

Sec 12.1   Introduction

From an analysis standpoint, the 4:1 Unun can be said to have received the most attention in the literature. It began with Ruthroff's introduction and complete analysis of this device in his classic paper published in 1959.[9] Ruthroff's paper then became the industry standard for this class of devices known as *transmission line transformers*. These are devices that transmit the energy from the input to the output by an efficient transmission line mode, and not by flux linkages (as in conventional transformers).

However 15 years earlier, Guanella had introduced, in his classic 1944 paper,[3] the first broadband Baluns by combining coiled transmission lines in a series-parallel arrangement, yielding ratios of $1:n^2$ where n = 1, 2, 3,... and so on. It has also been shown that Guanella's technique also lends itself to Ununs as well.[2] In fact, in this chapter, you will see that his technique of summing voltages of equal delays promises to yield high-power designs capable of operating on the VHF and UHF bands.

The 4:1 Unun also exemplifies (more than any other transformer) the many choices that can be made in its design. These include: 1) Ruthroff's or Guanella's designs, 2) wire or coaxial cable transmission lines, 3) coiled or beaded lines, 4) rods or toroids, 5) low-power or high-power designs, 6) HF, VHF, or UHF designs, and 7) the trade-offs in efficiency for low-frequency response or for high VSWR. The 4:1 Unun is the most prevalent of all the Ununs. It finds extensive use in solid-state circuits and in many antenna applications involving the matching of ground-fed antennas—where impedances of 12 to 13 ohms must be matched to 50-ohm coaxial cable. This chapter provides information on many 4:1 Unun designs.

Sec 12.2   The Ruthroff 4:1 Unun

Figure 12-1 illustrates two versions of Ruthroff's approach to obtaining a 4:1 unbalanced-to-unbalanced transformer (Unun). As can be seen, one uses a coiled wire transmission line, while the other uses a coiled coaxial cable. Depending upon the frequency, beaded transmission lines may also be used.

Ruthroff's design uses a single transmission line connected in, what I call, the bootstrap configuration. That is, terminal 2 is connected to terminal 3, lifting the transmission line (at the high-impedance side) by the voltage V_1. If the reactance of the coiled winding or beaded line is much greater than R_G, then only flux-canceling transmission line currents are allowed to flow. It is also apparent that the output voltage is the sum of a direct voltage, V_1, and a delayed voltage,

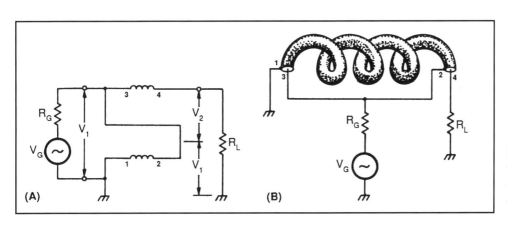

Figure 12-1. *The Ruthroff 4:1 Unun ($R_L=4R_G$): (A) coiled bifilar winding; (B) coiled coaxial cable.*

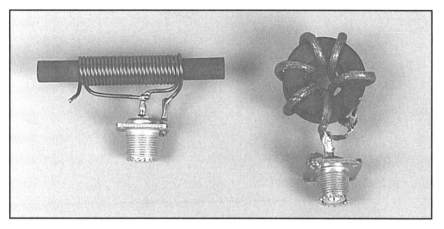

Photo 12-A. *Two versions of the Ruthroff 4:1 (50:12.5-ohm) Unun: coiled wire rod (on the left); coiled coaxial cable toroid (on the right).*

V_2, which traverses a single transmission line. This delay in V_2 eventually limits the high-frequency response. For example, if the electrical length of the line is a 1/2 wave, the output is zero. Ruthroff also found that the optimum value of the characteristic impedance of the transmission line (for maximum high-frequency response) is $R_L/2$.

Therefore, the electrical length and characteristic impedance of the transmission line play major roles in Ruthroff's design. Because his work was mainly concerned with small-signal applications, Ruthroff was able to obtain broad bands of a few tens of kilohertz to over a thousand megahertz. This was possible because he used a few turns (5 to 10) of fine wire (Nos. 37 and 38) on high-permeability toroids as small as 0.08 inches in OD. As a result, the phase-delay with these very short transmission lines was very small. However, large-signal (power) applications present an entirely different picture. For operation in the HF band (including 160 meters), transmission lines vary between one to three feet in length (depending upon impedance level). Consequently,

phase-delay can play a major role, as will be seen in the following examples.

Sec. 12.2.1   50:12.5-ohm Ununs

Photo 12-A shows two examples of efficient and broadband 4:1 Ununs matching 50 to 12.5 ohms. The rod version (on the left) has 14 bifilar turns of No. 14 H Thermaleze wire on a low-permeability (125) ferrite rod 0.375 inches in diameter and 3.5 inches long. The connections are shown in **Figure 12-1A**. The cable connector is on the low-impedance side. The response is flat from 1.5 to 30 MHz. In a matched condition, this Unun can easily handle the full legal limit of amateur radio power. Because a tightly wound rod Unun yields a characteristic impedance very close to 25 ohms (the optimum value), this is quite likely the easiest one to construct that covers the above bandwidth.

The toroidal version (on the right in **Photo 12-A**) has 6 turns of homemade, low-impedance coaxial cable on a 1.5-inch OD ferrite toroid with a permeability of 250. The connections are shown in **Figure**

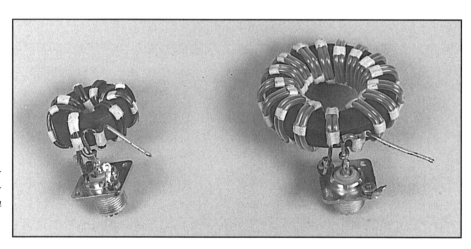

Photo 12-B. *Two higher-impedance Ruthroff 4:1 Ununs: 100:25-ohm (on the left); 200:50-ohm (on the right).*

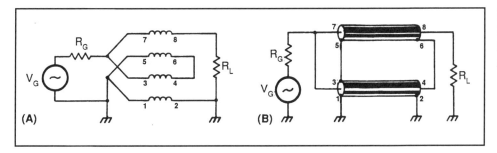

Figure 12-2. *The Guanella 4:1 Unun ($R_L=4R_G$): (A) coiled bifilar windings; (B) coiled or beaded coaxial cables.*

12-1B. The cable connector is on the low-impedance side. The inner conductor is No. 14 H Thermaleze wire and is covered with Teflon tubing. The outer braid is from a small coaxial cable (or from 1/8-inch tubular braid) tightly wrapped with Scotch No. 92 tape in order to obtain the desired characteristic impedance. In matching 50 to 12.5 ohms, the response is flat from 1.5 to 50 MHz. Because the current is evenly distributed on the inner conductor, this small Unun has an exceptionally high power capability—at least 5 kW of continuous power and 10 kW of peak power (in a matched condition).

Sec 12.2.2   100:25-ohm Unun

In some combiner applications, an Unun matching 100 to 25 ohms is required. The smaller toroidal version, pictured on the left in **Photo 12-B**, shows a Ruthroff design that can satisfy many of these requirements. It has 8 bifilar turns of No. 14 H Thermaleze wire on a 1.5-inch OD ferrite toroid with a permeability of 250. One wire is also covered with a single layer of Scotch No. 92 tape, providing a characteristic impedance close to the desired value of 50 ohms. In matching 100 to 25 ohms, the response is essentially flat from 1.5 to 30 MHz. This Unun can easily handle the full legal limit of amateur radio power.

Sec 12.2.3   200:50-ohm Unun

When dealing with this type of Balun, the Ruthroff approach cannot yield the broadband response of the lower-impedance designs shown above. Because more turns are required in order to obtain the necessary choking reactance, and a 100-ohm characteristic impedance that requires more spacing between the wires is used, the cores must be considerably larger. This results in longer transmission lines. Consequently, the high-frequency response is now limited by the greater phase delay of this high-impedance Unun.

The larger transformer, shown on the right in **Photo 12-B** is my optimized version of a Ruthroff 200:50-

ohm Unun. It has 16 bifilar turns of No. 14 H Thermaleze wire on a low-permeability (250) 2.4-inch OD ferrite toroid. Each wire is covered with Teflon tubing, resulting in a characteristic impedance of 97 ohms. Because of the long transmission line (36 inches), the impedance transformation ratio (in matching 200 ohms to 50 ohms) varies from 4 to 4.44 from 1.5 to 30 MHz. A conservative power rating (under a matched condition) is 2 kW of continuous power and 4 kW of peak power. Because this higher-impedance Unun has a larger voltage drop along the length of its windings, its loss (a dielectric-type[2]) is a little greater than the lower-impedance Ununs described earlier. In a matched condition, the efficiency is about 97 percent, while the others experience efficiencies of 98 to 99 percent.

Sec 12.3   The Guanella 4:1 Unun

Even though Guanella's investigation[3] was directed toward developing a broadband Balun to match the balanced output of a 100-watt, push-pull, vacuum-tube amplifier to the unbalanced load of a coaxial

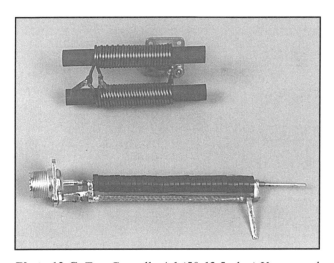

Photo 12-C. *Two Guanella 4:1 (50:12.5-ohm) Ununs: rod version (on the top), 1.5 to 50 MHz; beaded version (on the bottom), 10 MHz to over 100 MHz.*

cable, his technique of connecting transmission lines in a parallel-series arrangement has only recently been recognized as the design for the widest possible bandwidth in an unbalanced-to-unbalanced application.[2] Some have labeled his approach the "equal-delay network".[26] The major difference in Guanella's approach (from Ruthroff's) is that by summing the equal-delay voltages of coiled (or beaded) transmission lines, he minimizes the dependence of the high-frequency response on the lengths of the transmission lines. As was mentioned before, Ruthroff's method of summing a direct voltage with a delayed voltage that traversed a single transmission line has a limited application, especially with high-power, high-impedance Ununs (like 200:50 and 300:75 ohms).

Furthermore, Guanella's approach is also important in designing high- and low-impedance Baluns and Ununs with impedance transformation ratios other than 4:1. Connecting three transmission lines in parallel-series results in a 9:1 ratio, four in a 16:1. Also by connecting a fractional-ratio Unun in series with his Baluns, or by using various combinations of parallel-series transmission lines,[26,27] Ununs and Baluns are now available with a continuum of ratios from 1.36:1 to 16:1. Moreover, these ratios now make it possible to match 50-ohm cable to impedances as low as 3.125 ohms and as high as 800 ohms. A major factor in the success of these designs rests in the understanding of the low-frequency models of these various transformers.[2] This section looks at the 4:1 Unun using Guanella's approach. As in the Ruthroff case, the opti-

mum value of the characteristic impedances of the transmission lines for a Guanella 4:1 transformer is also $R_L/2$.

Sec 12.3.1   50:12.5-ohm Ununs

Figure 12-2 shows the schematic diagrams of the coiled-wire and coaxial cable (coiled or beaded) versions of 4:1 Ununs using Guanella's technique of connecting transmission lines in parallel-series arrangements. As can be seen in **Figure 12-2**, the lower transmission lines are grounded at both ends and, therefore, have no potential drop along their lengths. Thus, the coiling or beading has no effect. The core only acts as a mechanical support and the beads can be removed. In essence, the bottom transmission line plays the important role of a delay line. In addition, the low-frequency response of this form of Unun is solely determined by the reactance of the top coiled or beaded transmission line.

The top Unun in **Photo 12-C** shows a rod version of Guanella's 4:1 Unun. There are 13.5 bifilar turns of No. 14 H Thermaleze wire on low-permeability (125) ferrite rods 0.375 inches in diameter and 3.5 inches long. For ease of connection, one winding is clockwise and the other is counterclockwise. The cable connector is on the high-impedance side. In matching 50 to 12.5 ohms, the response is flat from 1.5 to over 50 MHz! This Unun, in a matched condition, is capable of handling the full legal limit of amateur radio power. Furthermore, with the 50-ohm generator on the right (in **Figure 12-2A**) and a 12.5-ohm balanced load on the left (perhaps a Yagi beam), this transformer makes an excellent step-down Balun.

The bottom transformer in **Photo 12-C** shows a beaded-coax version of a 50:12.5-ohm step-down Unun designed for 2-meter operation. It has 3.5 inches of beaded coax on the top transmission line (**Figure 12-2B**) and no beads on the bottom transmission line. (Actually, the bottom rod in **Figure 12-2A** can also be removed with no change in performance.) The beads are low-permeability (125) ferrite. The inner conductor of the coaxial cable is No. 12 H Thermaleze wire with about 3.5 layers of Scotch No. 92 tape (two 0.5-inch tapes wound edgewise like a window shade), providing a characteristic impedance close to the optimum value. The outer braid is from a small coaxial cable (or from 1/8-inch tubular braid). This homemade coax is further wrapped tightly with Scotch No. 92 tape in order to preserve its low characteristic impedance. The cable connector is on the low-

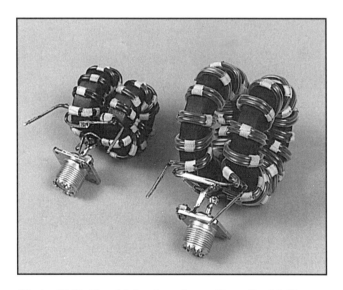

Photo 12-D. *Two higher-impedance Guanella 4:1 Ununs: 100:25-ohm (on the left); 200:50-ohm (on the right).*

impedance side. The response of this Unun is essentially flat from 10 to 100 MHz (the limit of my bridge). It can also (easily) handle the full legal limit of amateur radio power.

Sec 12.3.2   100:25-ohm Unun

The Unun on the left in **Photo 12-D** is a Guanella version that matches 100 to 25 ohms. There are 8 bifilar turns of No. 14 H Thermaleze wire on each 1.5-inch OD low-permeability (250) toroid. One toroid is wound clockwise and the other is wound counterclockwise. One of the wires (on each toroid) is covered with one layer of Scotch No. 92 tape. The cable connector is on the low-impedance side. The response is flat from 1.5 MHz to well over 30 MHz. This Unun can also handle the full legal limit of amateur radio power.

It is interesting to note that when used as a Balun (the ground removed from terminal 2), and placed in series (on the left side) with a 1.78:1 Unun (see **Chapter 13**), this compound arrangement provides an excellent Balun for matching 50-ohm coaxial cable directly to quad antennas having impedances of 100 to 110 ohms.

Sec 12.3.3   200:50-ohm Unun

The transformer on the right in **Photo 12-D** is an excellent Unun (or Balun with terminal 2 removed from ground) for matching 50 to 200 ohms. It has 14 bifilar turns of No. 14 H Thermaleze wire on each low-permeability (250) toroid with a 2.4-inch OD. Each wire is covered with Teflon tubing, providing a characteristic impedance of 98 ohms (which is quite good because the optimum value is 100). Again, for ease of connection, one winding is clockwise and the other is counterclockwise. When operating as an Unun or a Balun and matching 50 to 200 ohms, the response is essentially flat from 1.5 to 30 MHz. A conservative power rating (in a matched condition) is 5 kW of continuous power and 10 kW of peak power. This transformer has been reported to handle peak pulses of 10,000 volts!

Summary

Since its introduction by Ruthroff in 1959,[9] the 4:1 Unun has been the most popular transmission line transformer matching unbalanced impedances to unbalanced impedances. As I mentioned at the beginning of this chapter, there are many choices to consider when designing these broadband and efficient transformers. One of the most important choices involves whether to use the Ruthroff or Guanella approach. In fact, the Guanella design should probably be designated a *Balun/Unun*. Recently, it has become the design of choice in the higher frequency bands. From the designs presented in this chapter, I offer the following recommendations:

1. For Ununs in the HF band with impedance levels of 100:25 ohms and lower, the Ruthroff approach is recommended because of its simplicity.

2. For high impedance levels in the HF band (like 200:50 and 300:75 ohms), the Guanella approach is recommended.

3. For low-impedance operation on the VHF band, the beaded-coax Guanella approach is recommended.

4. For high-impedance operation on the VHF band, the coiled-wire Guanella approach appears to be the preferred choice, and should be investigated first. Obviously, the number of turns should be reduced from the examples shown in this chapter because the reactance of the winding is proportional to the frequency.

5. For high-power use on the HF band, the Ruthroff Unun with low-impedance coaxial cable on a toroid (on the right on **Photo 12-A**) is recommended. It is easy to construct and can very likely handle more than 5 kW of continuous power.

6. Also, at high-impedance levels, one might consider using lower permeability ferrites for higher efficiencies. Look at permeabilities of 125 and 40.

Chapter 13

1.33:1, 1.5:1, and 2:1 Ununs

Sec 13.1 Introduction

Little practical design information has been available on Ununs with impedance transformation ratios of less than 4:1 (these are called *fractional-ratio* Ununs). However, many important applications can be found for efficient and broadband Ununs with ratios like 1.33:1, 1.5:1, and 2:1. Some examples include the matching of 50-ohm coaxial cable to: a) vertical antennas, inverted Ls, and ground-fed slopers (all over good ground systems), b) 75-ohm hardline cable, c) a junction of two 50-ohm coaxial cables, d) shunt-fed towers performing as vertical antennas, and e) the output of a transceiver or class B linear amplifier when an unfavorable VSWR condition exists.

These three Ununs also play an important role in making other useful Baluns possible. Examples given in earlier chapters include: a) connecting a 1.5:1 Unun (50:75 ohms) in series with a 1:1 Balun (75:75 ohms) results in a broadband 1.5:1 Balun (50:75 ohms); b) connecting a 2:1 Unun (50:100 ohms) in series with a 1:1 Balun (100:100 ohms) results in a broadband 2:1 Balun (50:100 ohms); c) connecting a 1.5:1 Unun (50:75 ohms) in series with a 4:1 Balun (75:300 ohms) results in a broadband 6:1 Balun (50:300 ohms), and d) connecting a 1.33:1 Unun (50:66.7 ohms) in series with a 9:1 Balun (66.7:600 ohms) results in a broadband 12:1 Balun (50:600 ohms).

It has been shown[2] that a continuum of ratios can now be obtained with Ununs matching 50-ohm cable to impedances as low as 3.125 ohms and as high as 800 ohms. In addition, by using higher-order windings (trifilar, quadfilar, etc.), Ununs can be constructed with two broadband ratios like 1.5:1 and 3:1, or 2:1 and 4:1. Furthermore, by tapping some of the windings of these higher-order Ununs, multimatch transformers can be constructed with many broadband ratios. As a result of this class of fractional-ratio Ununs, a continuum of Ununs and Baluns is now available to match 50 ohms unbalanced to unbalanced or balanced impedances as low as 3.125 ohms and as high as 800 ohms.

My first attempt to obtain ratios less than 4:1 was made by tapping one of the wires in a Ruthroff 4:1 bifilar Unun. My experiment met with only moderate success.[2] An adequate low-frequency response with a 1.33:1 ratio was difficult to obtain. Also, the 2:1 ratio had considerably greater loss than higher or lower ratios. Recently, I found that higher-order windings (trifilar, quadrifilar, etc.), some with taps, provide much wider bandwidths and higher efficiencies. This

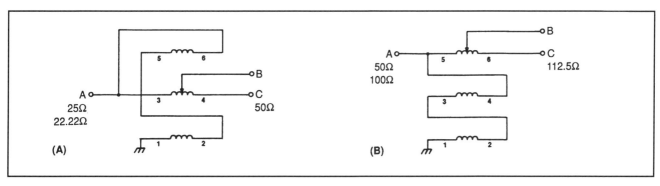

Figure 13-1. *Schematic diagrams: (A) matching 50 to 25 ohms (B-A) and 50 to 22.22 ohms (C-A); (B) matching 100 to 50 ohms (B-A) and 112.5 to 50 ohms (C-A).*

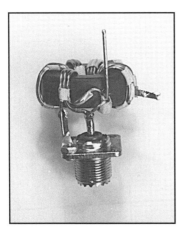

Photo 13-A. *Bottom view of the 2:1 Unun designed to match 50 ohms to 25 ohms or 22.2 ohms (Figure 13-1A). The connector is on the low-impedance side.*

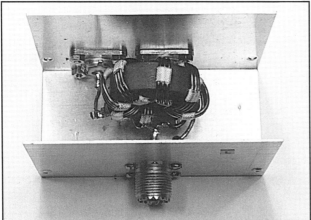

Photo 13-B. *The 2:1 Unun mounted in a 4 inch long by 2 inch wide by 2.75 inch high minibox.*

chapter describes fractional-ratio Ununs using these higher-order windings.

The next section discusses the practical aspects of the 2:1 Unun. This Unun is not only one of the more useful transformers, but it also serves as a good introduction to the trifilar and quadrifilar designs. What follows is an introduction to the most difficult fractional-ratio Unun—the quintufilar design, which results in very broadband 1.33:1 and 1.5:1 Ununs. A more complete discussion appears in **Part I** of this book.

This chapter closes with construction tips. As you will see, these Ununs can be difficult to construct.

Sec 13.2   2:1 Ununs

Figure 13-1A shows the schematic diagram of an Unun designed to match 50-ohm cable to an unbalanced load of 25 ohms (2:1 ratio with connections A-B) or 22.22 ohms (2.25:1 ratio with connections A-C). It has 6 trifilar turns of No. 14 H Thermaleze wire on a 1.5-inch OD ferrite toroid with a permeability of

250. Winding 3-4 is tapped at 5 turns from terminal 3. **Photo 13-A** is a photograph showing the various connections. The connector is on the low-impedance side. **Photo 13-B** shows the transformer mounted in a CU-3015A (4 inches long by 2 inches wide by 2.75 inches high) minibox. In matching 50 ohms to either 25 or 22.22 ohms, the transformation ratio is constant from 1 to 30 MHz.

Because the transmission lines are very short, this Unun does quite well as a step-up transformer. That is, when matching 50 ohms (on the left side) to 100 ohms (connections A-B) or 112.5 ohms (connections A-C) on the right side, the transformation ratio is constant from 1 to 15 MHz. Because of the extremely high efficiency of this transformer (98 to 99 percent under matched conditions), this small version can easily handle the full legal limit of amateur radio power.

Figure 13-1B shows the schematic diagram of an Unun designed to match 50-ohm cable to an unbalanced load of 100 ohms (2:1 ratio with connections A-B) or 112.5-ohms (2.25:1 ratio with connections A-C). It has 7 trifilar turns on a 1.5-inch OD ferrite toroid with a permeability of 250. The top winding 5-6 is No. 14 Thermaleze wire and is tapped at 6 turns from terminal 5. The other two windings are No. 16 H Thermaleze wire. **Photo 13-C** shows the various connections. The connector is on the low-impedance side. In matching 50-ohm cable to 100 ohms (A-B) or 112.5 ohms (A-C), the transformation ratio is constant from 1 to 30 MHz.

Again, because the transmission lines are very short, this Unun does quite well as a step-down transformer. In matching 50-ohm cable (on the right side) to 25 ohms (A-B) or 22.22 ohms (A-C), the transformation ratios are constant from 1 to 15 MHz. As above, this transformer can easily handle the full legal limit of amateur radio power.

Although the quadrifilar Unun shown in the schematic diagram in **Figure 13-2** and in **Photo 13-D** has an impedance transformation ratio of 1.78:1, it should also satisfy many of the 2:1 requirements. This Unun, which is designed to match 50-ohm cable to an unbalanced load of 28 ohms, not only has a very broadband response (1 MHz to over 50 MHz), but also offers other possible wideband ratios that will be covered in succeeding chapters.

Specifically, the Unun has 5 quadrifilar turns on a 1.5-inch OD ferrite toroid with a permeability of 250. Winding 5-6 is No. 14 H Thermaleze wire and the other three are No. 16 H Thermaleze wire. Like the

Photo 13-C. *Bottom view of the 2:1 Unun designed to match 50 ohms to 100 ohms or 112.5 ohms (Figure 13-1B). The connector is on the low-impedance side.*

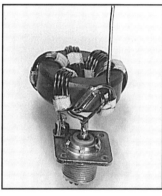

Photo 13-D. *Bottom view of the 1.78:1 Unun designed to match 50 to 28 ohms. The connector is on the low-impedance side.*

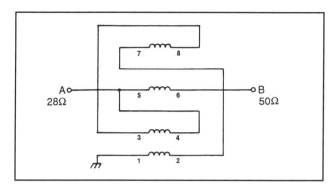

Figure 13-2. *Schematic diagram of the quadrifilar Unun designed to match 50 to 28 ohms (1.78:1 ratio).*

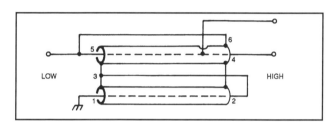

Figure 13-3. *Schematic diagram of a tapped-trifilar Unun that uses two sections of coaxial cable, yielding impedance ratios of 2:1 and 2.25:1.*

two 2:1 Ununs described above, this one also easily handles the full legal limit of amateur radio power.

As with most coiled Ununs that have little spacing between adjacent turns, current-crowding (between adjacent turns) can eventually limit the power-handling capability of these devices. It's possible to improve the ability for handling higher currents by using thicker wires, or by using coaxial cables where current-crowding is nonexistent. **Figure 13-3** shows the schematic diagram of a tapped-trifilar transformer that uses two sections of coaxial cable yielding impedance ratios of 2:1 and 2.25:1. **Photo 13-E** shows two trifilar toroidal transformers using low-impedance coaxial cables with their outer braids connected in parallel and acting as the third conductor. These transformers are conservatively rated at 5 kW of continuous power.

The smaller transformer in **Photo 13-E** has 7 trifilar turns of low-impedance coax on a 2-inch OD toroid with a permeability of 290. The No. 14 H Thermaleze wire inner conductors have four layers of Scotch No. 92 tape. The outer braids are made from small coaxial cables (or 1/8-inch tubular braid), and are also wrapped with Scotch No. 92 tape in order to preserve the low characteristic impedances. The inner conductor of the top coax in **Figure 13-3** is tapped at 6 turns

from terminal 5. When matching 50 ohms to 22.22 ohms or 25 ohms, the impedance ratio is constant from 1 to over 50 MHz.

The larger transformer in **Photo 13-E** also has 7 trifilar turns, but on a 2.4-inch OD toroid with a permeability of 125. The inner conductors of No. 14 H Thermaleze wire now have a 15-mil wall of Teflon sleeving, yielding the low-impedance coaxial cable. The outer braids are the same. Because the ferrite permeability is lower and the lengths of the transmission lines are longer than those of the smaller unit, this transformer's bandwidth is not quite as good. When matching 50 to 22.22 ohms (this particular Unun doesn't have a tapped winding), the impedance ratio is constant from 1.7 to 30 MHz.

Although not shown, these very high-powered 2:1 Ununs can also be easily designed to match 50-ohm cable to unbalanced loads of 100 and 112.5 ohms. This is done by using small but high-powered coaxes like RG-303/U, RG-141/U, or RG-142/U.

Sec 13.3   1.5:1 Ununs

Figure 13-4 shows three basic forms of a quintufilar 1.56:1 Unun that should satisfy most of the 1.5:1 requirements. As can be seen, the only difference in

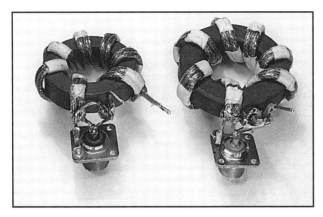

Photo 13-E. *Two toroidal transformers using coaxial cable and designed to match 50 to 22.22 ohms (2.25:1). The smaller transformer is also tapped, yielding a match of 50 to 25 ohms (2:1).*

the schematic diagrams is in the interleaving of the windings. This is done to optimize the performance of these Ununs at the various impedance levels. Schematic A is optimized for matching 50 to 75 ohms. Schematic B is optimized for matching 32 to 50 ohms. Schematic C, while optimized for matching 40 to 62 ohms, still yields quite broadband ratios at both 50:75 and 32:50-ohm levels. It should be a useful, general-purpose Unun.

Photo 13-F is a photograph of the bottom views (showing the connections) of the three different designs. They appear in the same order as the schematics of **Figure 13-4**; i.e., a) the Unun on the left is designed to match 50 to 75 ohms, b) the Unun in the center is design to match 32 to 50 ohms, and c) the

Unun on the right is designed to work quite well at both impedance levels. The SO-239 connectors are all on the low impedance side of the Ununs.

All three transformers have four quintufilar turns on a 1.5-inch OD ferrite toroid with a permeability of 250. Their differences are:

1. **50:75 ohms** (on the left on **Figure 13-4** and **Photo 13-F**).

Winding 9-10 is No. 14 H Thermaleze wire. The other four windings are No. 16 H Thermaleze wire. When matching 50 to 75 ohms (actually to 78 ohms), the transformation ratio is constant from 1 to over 30 MHz. In matching 50 ohms (on the right side in **Figure 13-3A**) to 32 ohms, it is still constant from 1 to 15 MHz.

2. **32:50 ohms** (in the center in **Figure 13-4** and **Photo 13-F**).

Winding 5-6 is No. 14 H Thermaleze wire. The other four windings are No. 16 H Thermaleze wire. When matching 32 to 50 ohms, the transformation ratio is constant from 1 to over 30 MHz. In matching 75 ohms (on the right side in **Figure 13-3B**) to 50 ohms, it is still constant from 1 to 15 MHz.

3. **50:75 ohms; 32:50 ohms** (on the right in **Figure 13-4** and **Photo 13-F**).

Winding 7-8 is No. 14 H Thermaleze wire. The other four windings are No. 16 H Thermaleze wire. In matching 32 to 50 ohms, the transformation ratio is constant from 1 to 30 MHz. In matching 75 ohms (on the right side in **Figure 13-3C**) to 50 ohms, it is still constant to 21 MHz. This is quite a good general-purpose design.

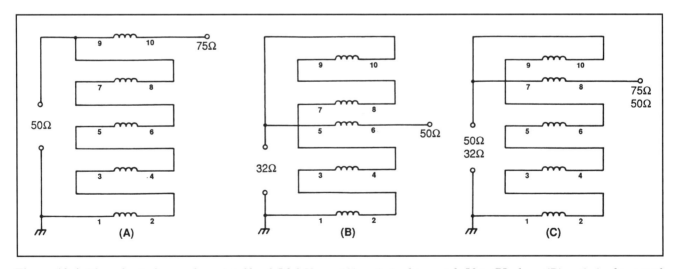

Figure 13-4. *Three basic forms of a quintufilar 1.56:1 Unun: (A) optimized to match 50 to 75 ohms, (B) optimized to match 32 to 50 ohms, and (C) optimized to match 40 to 62 ohms, resulting in a good general-purpose design.*

Even though a small toroid (with only a 1.5-inch OD) is used, these Ununs are still very sturdy transformers. Because their efficiencies are so high (98 to 99 percent), they can easily handle the full legal limit of amateur radio power.[2] Furthermore, the windings carrying the majority of the current (80 percent) are all No. 14 wire. Only when well-designed Ununs are subjected to very high VSWRs will excessive heating occur. Ununs (and Baluns) should never be exposed to these severe conditions.

Sec 13.4   A 1.33:1 Unun

The circuit shown in **Figure 13-5** evolved after many attempts were made at obtaining a broadband match of 50 to 66.7 ohms (1.33:1). **Photo 13-G** shows the bottom view of an actual design. The SO-239 connector is on the low impedance side. **Photo 13-H** shows the Unun mounted in a CU-3015A minibox.

Specifically, this Unun has five quintufilar turns on a 1.5-inch OD ferrite toroid with a permeability of 250. Winding 5-6 is No. 14 H Thermaleze wire and is tapped at three turns from terminal 5 (**Figure 13-4**). It is also covered with one layer of Scotch No. 92 polyimide tape, optimizing the performance at the 50:66.7-ohm level. The other four windings are No. 16 H Thermaleze wire.

In matching 50 to 66.7 ohms (A-B), the transformation ratio is practically constant from 1 to 30 MHz. The ratio only decreases by 3 percent across the band. In matching 50 to 32 ohms (C-A), the transformation ratio is constant from 1 to 30 MHz. In matching 75 to 50 ohms (C-A), the ratio is constant from 1 to 15 MHz. In matching 50 to 37.6 ohms (B-A), the ratio is constant from 1 to 15 MHz. As you can see, the Unun has some useful broadband multimatches.

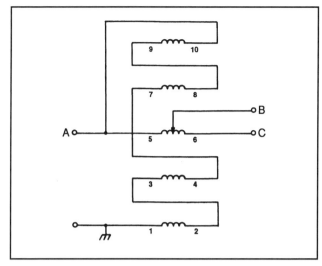

Figure 13-5. *Schematic diagram of a quintufilar Unun specifically designed to yield a broadband 1.33:1 ratio (66.7:50 ohms; connection B-A). Connection C-A also yields a broadband 1.56:1 ratio (50:32 ohms).*

As in the cases of the other three Ununs, this tapped-Unun also easily handles the full legal limit of amateur radio power. Like the 2:1 Unun, for higher power capabilities, thicker wires or a three-coax quintufilar design can be used.[2]

Sec 13.5   Construction Tips

Most of my Unun designs use the bootstrap connection that sums direct voltages (on the high-impedance side) with a delayed voltage, which traverses a single transmission line.[2] Therefore, in order to achieve the very wideband responses, small toroids (which allow the shortest transmission lines) are used. The small 1.5-inch OD toroids offer this advantage. Furthermore,

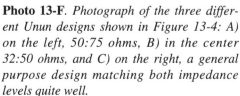

Photo 13-F. *Photograph of the three different Unun designs shown in Figure 13-4: A) on the left, 50:75 ohms, B) in the center 32:50 ohms, and C) on the right, a general purpose design matching both impedance levels quite well.*

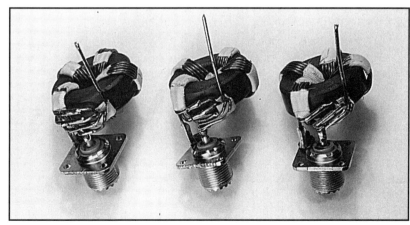

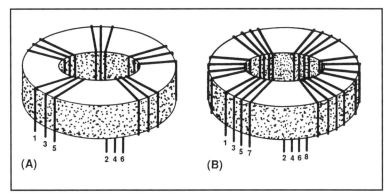

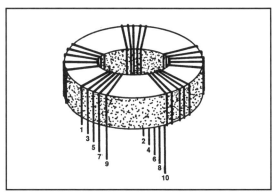

Figure 13-6. *Pictorials of higher-order windings: (A) trifilar and (B) quadrifilar.*

Figure 13-7. *Pictorial of a quintufilar winding.*

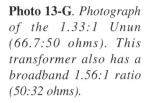

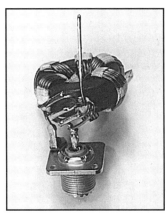

Photo 13-G. *Photograph of the 1.33:1 Unun (66.7:50 ohms). This transformer also has a broadband 1.56:1 ratio (50:32 ohms).*

quintufilar (and higher-order windings) Ununs are also eventually limited in their high-frequency responses by self-resonances. Shorter winding lengths keep these self-resonances well out of the HF band. For the Ununs in this chapter, they occur between 45 and 65 MHz, with **Figure 13-4A** having the higher value.

There is also a mechanical advantage in using the smaller toroids. You'll find that the popular CU-3015A minibox makes an excellent enclosure for the 1.5-inch OD toroid. Furthermore, because ferrite is a ceramic and, therefore, unaffected by moisture, no special precautions need be taken for out-of-doors use. Potting the transformer in plastic is unnecessary. One must only keep the Unun out of a pool of water.

Because well-designed transformers have virtually no flux in the core, their power ratings are mainly determined by the ability of the transmission lines to handle the voltages and currents. Furthermore, it can be shown that the losses in these transformers are related to the voltage gradients along the transmission lines.[2] Thus, they are dielectric-type ferrite losses. This means that the efficiency can be severely degrad-

ed with very high VSWRs since higher voltage gradients occur under these conditions.

Several suggestions can be made regarding the construction of Ununs using these higher-order windings (trifilar, quadrifilar, etc.). They are:

1) Make a ribbon out of the wires and wind them all at the same time. This keeps the wires as close as possible, resulting in the maintenance of the optimum characteristic impedance of the transmission lines. I found that strips made with 1.25- by 0.375- to 0.55-inch glass tape (Scotch No. 27), clamped about every 1/2 inch, hold the wires in place very well. The starting lengths of the wires should be about 5 inches longer than one would calculate knowing the number of turns and the length around each turn.

2) Because work-hardening of the copper wire takes place in coiling it around a toroid, a pair of pliers and

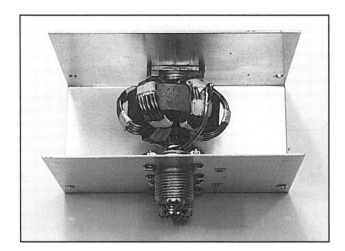

Photo 13-H. *The 1.33:1 Unun mounted in a CU-3015A minibox.*

a strong thumb (and arms) are indispensable tools. It takes considerable effort to wind these transformers. Also, because these designs have adequate margins at their low-frequency ends, some space between the windings and the toroids can be tolerated.

3) It is helpful to recognize the various patterns that appear at the ends of the windings. **Figure 13-6** shows a drawing of the trifilar and quadrifilar patterns and **Figure 13-7** shows the quintufilar pattern. Note that terminal 1 and terminal 6 or terminal 8 or 10 are the outside terminals of the patterns. Also, note that terminal 1 is always grounded in the schematic diagrams.

4) Tapping windings can be one of the more difficult tasks in constructing these transformers. Winding a tapped transformer is also more difficult. I found that the edge of a small, fine file does the best job in removing the insulation. About 1/8 to 1/4 inch is removed around the wire. It also helps to remove some of the copper. Then a flat 1/8-inch copper strip

or No. 14 wire flattened on one end is soldered to the bare wire. The soldered connection is then rendered smooth using the edge of the file. Finally, two pieces of Scotch No. 92 polyimide tape are placed on the joint to insulate it from the neighboring turns. I also found that a tap placed one turn from the end of the winding is best made approximately 4 inches from the end of the wire (when the wire is straight).

Finally, a comment should be made about low-power Ununs. Practically all of the transformers in this chapter can be easily designed for low-power use. Designs capable of handing the full output of HF transceivers can be readily constructed. Cores with an OD of 1.25 inches are recommended. The same number of turns, but with one size smaller wire, is also recommended. Because smaller cores and thinner wires are used, these lower-power units are not only easier to construct, but they also have wider bandwidths due to the shorter lengths of the windings.

Chapter 14

Dual-Ratio Ununs

Sec 14.1 Introduction

Earlier chapters in this book on Ununs have basically covered single-ratio transformers. Broadband ratios of 1.33:1, 1.5:1, 2:1, and 4:1 were the design objectives. The 1.33:1 ratio was obtained by tapping a 1.5:1 (actually 1.56:1) quintufilar-wound Unun. The 2:1 ratio was obtained by tapping a 2.25:1 trifilar-wound Unun. Although these transformers can be considered to have two broadband ratios (1.33:1 and 1.56:1 or 2:1 and 2.25:1), their two ratios were not different enough for many practical applications. This is especially true of antennas where the input impedance varies with frequency.

My earlier work[2] and an article by Genaille[10] have shown that a host of ratios (less than 4:1) can be obtained by tapping the bifilar winding of a Ruthroff 4:1 Unun.[9] However, the bandwidths obtained using this technique are quite limited with each ratio and are highly dependent upon the impedance level. This is particularly true when a rod core is used because it

requires more turns (resulting in longer transmission lines) in order to obtain the necessary choking reactance that isolates the input from the output. Furthermore, ratios around 2:1 exhibit more loss because autotransformer action also enters into the matching process.[2]

By using quadrifilar and quintufilar windings on small 1.5-inch OD cores, and connecting them in such a way that the characteristic impedances of the windings are near optimum, two very different and broadband ratios matching 50 ohms to lower impedances are obtained. Furthermore, because the transmission lines in these transformers are so very short (8 to 9 inches in length), these transformers do quite well in matching 50 ohms to higher impedances (as step-up transformers).

This chapter presents two Ununs which have two broadband ratios that differ by a factor of two! One has a 1.5:1 and a 3:1 ratio (actually 1.56:1 and 2.78:1). The other has a 2:1 (actually 1.78:1) and a 4:1 ratio. Also, this chapter introduces the novel tech-

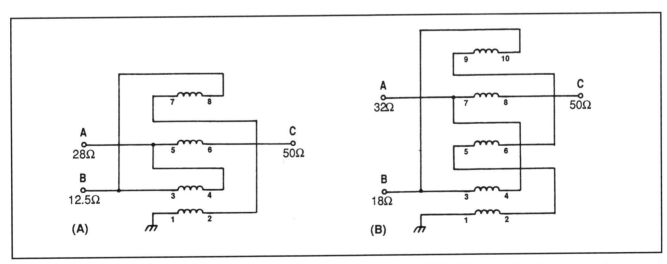

Figure 14-1. *Schematic diagrams of dual-ratio Ununs: (A) 1.78:1 connection C-A, 4:1 connection C-B; (B) 1.56:1 connection C-A, 2.78:1 connection C-B.*

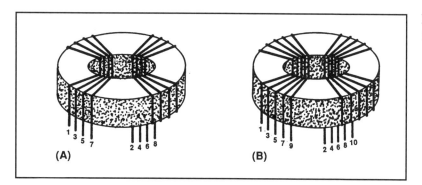

Figure 14-2. *Pictorials of higher-order windings: (A) quadrifilar, (B) quintufilar.*

nique of connecting these two transformers in parallel on their 50-ohm sides, resulting in four very broadband ratios.

Sec 14.2   2:1 and 4:1 Ratios

Figure 14-1A shows the schematic diagram of the quadrifilar Unun yielding ratios of 2:1 (actually 1.78:1) and 4:1. **Figure 14-2A** provides a pictorial of its windings. On the left in **Photo 14-A**, you see the bottom view of an Unun. The cable connector is on the 28-ohm (1.78:1) side. This Unun has four quadrifilar turns of No. 14 H Thermaleze wire on a 1.5-inch OD toroid with a permeability of 250.

In matching 50 to 28 ohms (connection C-A), the response is flat to within 1 percent from 1 to 30 MHz. From 1 to 50 MHz, it's flat to within 2 percent. In matching 50 to 12.5 ohms (connection C-B), the response is flat to within 3 percent from 1 to 30 MHz.

Because very short transmission lines are used, this transformer performs quite well as a step-up transformer. In matching 50 to 200 ohms (connection B-C), the response is flat to within 3 percent from 1.5 to

10 MHz. In matching 50 to 89 ohms (connection A-C), the response is flat to within 5 percent from 1.5 to 30 MHz!

Sec 14.2.1   Construction Tips

Start with about 14 inches of straightened wire. Form the wires into a ribbon with clamps of Scotch No. 27 glass tape every 1/2 inch. I found that strips 3/16 inch wide and about 1.5 inches long do a good job. The clamps should be long enough to go around the wires twice. After winding, connect terminals 2 and 7. Then connect terminals 3 and 8. Finally, connect terminals 4 and 5. Because work-hardening takes place quickly, you will find that a pair of pliers and a strong thumb (and arms) are necessary tools. You will also find that winding these exceptionally performing transformers is not easy. As in all endeavors, practice really pays off.

Sec 14.3   1.5:1 and 3:1 Ratios

Figure 14-1B shows the schematic diagram of the quintufilar Unun yielding ratios of 1.5:1 and 3:1

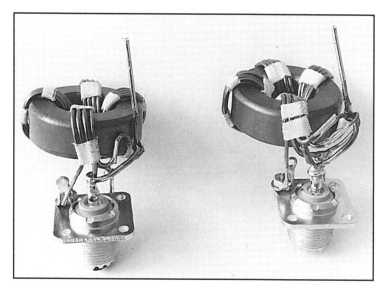

Photo 14-A. *On the left, a quadrifilar Unun with ratios of 1.78:1 and 4:1; on the right, a quintufilar Unun with ratios of 1.56:1 and 2.78:1.*

Photo 14-B. *The dual-ratio quintufilar Unun mounted in a 4 inch long by 2 inch wide by 2.75 inch high minibox.*

(actually 1.56:1 and 2.78:1). **Figure 14-2B** is a pictorial of its windings. On the right side in **Photo 14-A** you see a bottom view of an Unun. The cable connector is on the 32-ohm (1.56:1) side. This Unun has four quintufilar turns on a 1.5-inch OD toroid with a permeability of 250. Windings 3-4 and 7-8 are No. 14 H Thermaleze wire. The other three are No. 16 H Thermaleze wire. Winding 7-8 also has two layers of Scotch No. 92 polyimide tape, which optimizes the 1.56:1 ratio.

Photo 14-C. *The two dual-ratio Ununs connected in parallel on their 50-ohm sides providing four broadband ratios close to 1.5:1, 2:1, 3:1, and 4:1. The quadrifilar unit is on the left and the quintufilar unit is on the right. The enclosure is a 5 inch long by 3 inch wide by 2 inch high minibox.*

In matching 50 to 32 ohms (connection C-A), the response is essentially flat (less than 1 percent variation) from 1 MHz to over 40 MHz. Without the two layers of Scotch No. 92 tape, the response varies by 4 percent from 1 to 30 MHz. When used as a step-up transformer matching 50 to 78 ohms (connection A-C), and with the two layers of Scotch No. 92 tape on winding 7-8, the response is flat to within 5 percent from 1 to 15 MHz. Without the extra insulation on winding 7-8, the response is flat to within 5 percent from 1 to 7.5 MHz.

In matching 50 to 18 ohms (connection C-B), the variation in response is less than 3 percent from 1 to 40 MHz. The response is the same whether winding 7-8 is covered with the extra insulation or not. As a step-up transformer matching 50 to 139 ohms (connection B-C), the response is flat to within 3 percent from 1 to 10 MHz (with or without the extra insulation on winding 7-8). **Photo 14-B** shows this Unun mounted in a 4 inch long by 2 inch wide by 2.75 inch high minibox. The two cable connectors on the low impedance side could be replaced with feedthrough insulators for antenna use.

Sec 14.3.1   Construction Tips

Prepare the ribbon as was described for the quadrifilar Unun. If you choose to use the two extra layers of Scotch No. 92 tape on winding 7-8, make sure this winding is on the outside position of the ribbon (refer to **Figure 14-2B**). I found the best order in which to connect the wires is as follows: first, connect terminal 2 to 5; second, connect terminal 6 to 9; third, connect terminal 3 to 10; and, finally, connect terminal 4 to 7.

As was mentioned before, because a small toroid is used in order to achieve the best response (due to shorter transmission lines), this transformer also requires considerable strength and patience in the winding process.

Sec 14.4   Parallel Transformers

One of the most pleasant surprises I received with these efficient and broadband transformers was to find that they can be connected in parallel on their 50-ohm sides and still possess the same performance levels. Because the loading effect of one transformer on the other is minimal (like a short length of transmission line), the transformer that is properly terminated takes the power, while the other one is transparent. This lets you obtain four very wideband ratios with the two dual-ratio Ununs described in this chapter. Obviously, this technique eliminates one transmission line. Furthermore, Baluns can also be connected this way for feeding, with a single coaxial cable, beams and dipoles with different resonant impedances.

Photo 14-C shows two transformers connected in parallel on their 50-ohm sides using the two dual-ratio Ununs described in this chapter. As was mentioned, it now yields four wideband ratios very close to 1.5:1, 2:1, 3:1, and 4:1. I have used this matching network to feed a host of ground-fed antennas (over a good ground system). In one case, I had a 10-, 15-, and 20-meter trap vertical, slopers for 40 and 160 meters, a 12-meter vertical, and an inverted L for 80 meters all matched to a single coaxial cable at the same time. It was a simple matter of connecting each antenna to the output terminal that presented the best match (lowest VSWR). This technique is actually an extension of connecting dipoles for different bands, in parallel. The antenna that presents the correct impedance takes the power, and the others are essentially transparent. In many cases, I found that only one transformer with two broadband ratios performed adequately.

Chapter 15

Multimatch Ununs

Sec 15.1   Introduction

Broadband multimatch Ununs capable of high-power applications have been the goal of many designers over the years. Some have resorted to using conventional autotransformers with tapped windings to obtain the many impedance transformation ratios. However, these attempts met with little success because of the device's limited bandwidths and efficiencies. Others (including myself)[2] have tried tapping a bifilar Ruthroff Unun.[9] Although these designs yielded the high efficiencies of transmission line transformers, they had limited bandwidths. Furthermore, their best bandwidths (for the various ratios) occurred at odd impedance levels. In other words, they didn't meet the objective of broadband operation with one of the input or output ports at 50 ohms.

Chapter 14 presented two Ununs which had two broadband ratios that differed by a factor of two. One had a 1.5:1 and a 3:1 ratio (actually 1.56:1 and 2.78:1). The other had a 2:1 (actually 1.78:1) and a 4:1 ratio. This chapter describes two multimatch designs that are capable of many more broadband ratios. For the most part, both are capable of broadband operation from 1.7 to 30 MHz.

One Unun has the following five ratios (which are close to): 1.5:1, 2:1, 4:1, 6:1, and 9:1. Because the two lower ratios work well in either direction (that is

stepping up or down from 50 ohms), this design can match 50-ohm cable to impedances as high as 100 ohms (actually 112.5 ohms) and as low as 5.6 ohms over the frequency range. As a result, it has seven usable applications. Furthermore, because this is a transmission line transformer that cancels out the flux in the core, losses (in a matched condition) of only 0.04 to 0.08 dB can be expected.

The novelty in this design lies in the use of a trifilar winding (with one winding tapped) on a very small ferrite toroid, resulting in the shortest possible lengths of transmission lines. The windings are also connected in such a manner as to optimize their characteristic impedances from an overall standpoint.

I have used the adjective *ultimate* to describe the second Unun design. Although it might be risky business, I assume that this design will meet one of the most common definitions for this adjective—namely, *beyond which it is impossible to go.* For many of us, the classic use of this adjective was made by Lew McCoy in describing his popular transmatch.[22] Although there have been some improvements to Lew's design, his use of this definite (and strong) adjective can be said to have withstood the test of time. I hope my use meets with similar success.

While the tapped-trifilar design provides five broadband ratios and seven practical applications, the *ultimate* design presented in this chapter goes well

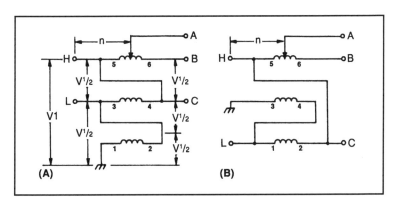

Figure 15-1. *Circuit diagrams for the 5-ratio Unun: (A) diagram for analysis; (B) transposed windings for best overall performance.*

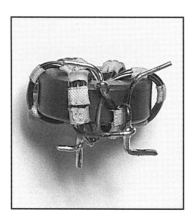

Photo 15-A. *Bottom view of the 5-ratio Unun of Figure 15-1B. The upper-left lead is terminal C. The upper-right lead is terminal B. The lower-left lead is terminal H. The lead pointing straight down is grounded (terminal 3). The lower-right lead is terminal L.*

beyond this number. It uses a tapped-quadrifilar design that yields the following 10 broadband ratios: 1.36:1, 1.56:1, 1.78:1, 2.25:1, 3.06:1, 4:1, 6.25:1, 9:1, 12.25:1, and 16:1. Because the four lower ratios also work quite well in either direction, this design offers *fourteen* applications in matching 50-ohm cable to impedances as high as 112.5 ohms and as low as 3.125 ohms. It also has the advantage of using a small low-loss toroidal core. Additionally, the windings are also interleaved in a pattern that optimizes their characteristic impedance.

However, this achievement comes at a price—*difficulty*. The 5-ratio Unun, which uses a trifilar winding, is considerably easier to wind. In addition, the quadrifilar 10-ratio Unun has two of its windings tapped, while the 5-ratio Unun has only one (see **Chapter 13** on tapping windings). If you have had little experience in winding Ununs or Baluns,

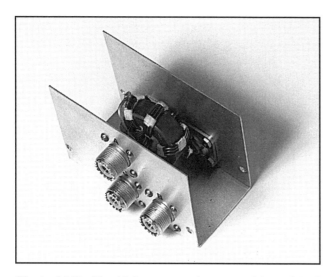

Photo 15-B. *The high-power unit mounted in a 4 inch long by 2 inch wide by 2.75 inch high minibox.*

attempt simplified versions of these two multimatch Ununs first. These versions eliminate the tapping of the windings. For the trifilar Unun, the remaining ratios would be: 2.25:1, 4:1, and 9:1. For the quadrifilar Unun, they would be: 1.78:1, 2.25:1, 4:1, 9:1, and 16:1.

For those interested in the design considerations of these broadband multimatch transformers, a brief review is presented in each section. These sections are followed by others describing high-power designs capable of handling the full legal limit of amateur radio power. Finally, the remaining sections present low-power designs capable of handling the output of any HF transceiver. Because transmission line transformers can be made so efficient in matching 50 to 100 ohms or less, their small sizes will surprise many readers. Therefore, the combination of using small ferrite toroids with the maximum allowable permeability (less than 300) for high efficiency,[2] and with sufficient turns to meet the low-frequency objective, results in the excellent performance exhibited by the designs in this chapter.

Sec 15.2   The 5-Ratio Unun

Let's first look at **Figure 15-1A** because it is the easiest form of the trifilar-wound Unun to explain. For example, if the input voltage to ground, V_1, is connected to terminal H, the output terminal B, has a voltage to ground of $3/2V_1$. This results in a transformation ratio, g, of $(3/2)^2$ or 2.25:1. This should satisfy most 2:1 requirements. If the output is at terminal A to ground, then the output voltage is:

$$V_o = V_1 + V_1(n/2N)$$
$$= V_1(1 + n/2N) \qquad \text{(Eq 15-1)}$$

where:
N = the total number of turns on the winding
n = the number of turns from terminal 5.

The transformation ratio, g, then becomes:

$$g = (V_o/V_1)^2$$
$$= (1 + n/2N)^2 \qquad \text{(Eq 15-2)}$$

If the input voltage to ground, V_1, is connected to terminal L, then terminal C has twice the voltage of V_1—resulting in a 4:1 ratio. Terminal B has three times the voltage resulting in a 9:1 ratio. With terminal A, the output voltage is:

$$V_o = 2V_1 + V_1(n/N)$$
$$= V_1(2 + n/N) \qquad \text{(Eq 15-3)}$$

The transformation ratio, g, then becomes:

$$g = (2 + n/N)^2 \qquad \text{(Eq 15-4)}$$

Sec 15.2.1   A High-power 5-Ratio Unun

After several attempts at rearranging the windings of **Figure 15-1A** for the best overall performance (optimizing the effective characteristic impedances of the windings), **Figure 15-1B** evolved. **Photo 15-A** shows the bottom view of an Unun, using the circuit of **Figure 15-1B**, capable of handling the full legal limit of amateur radio power. **Photo 15-B** shows the unit mounted in a CU-3015A minibox. It has five trifilar turns on a 1.5-inch OD ferrite toroid with a permeability of 250. Winding 5-6 is tapped at two turns (n = 2) from terminal 5.

If the 9:1 ratio matching 50 to 5.6 ohms (connection B-L) is to be used at full power, then winding 3-4 should be No. 12 H Thermaleze wire. If not, then all windings can be No. 14 H Thermaleze wire.

A listing of the expected performance across the band from 1.7 MHz to 30 MHz, with the various ratios, is as follows:

9:1 (B-L); 50:5.6 ohms
Ratio is within 1 percent!
5.75:1 (A-L); 50:8.7 ohms
Ratio decreases by 5 percent.
4:1 (C-L); 50:12.5 ohms
Ratio increases by 15 percent (the greatest deviation of all the ratios).
2.25:1
a) (B-H); 50:22.22 ohms
Ratio decreases by 4 percent.
b) (H-B); 50:112.5 ohms
Ratio increases by 8 percent.
1.44:1
a) (A-H); 50:35 ohms
Ratio decreases by 10 percent.
b) (H-A); 50:72 ohms
Ratio increases by 2 percent.

Photo 15-C. *The low-power unit mounted in a homemade 2 inch long by 1.5 inch wide by 2.25 inch high minibox.*

Several comments should be made regarding the expected results shown above. First of all, the greatest deviation from a flat response at any ratio occurs when matching 50 to 12.5 ohms (connection C-L; a 4:1 ratio). If an accurate insertion loss measurement was made at this ratio and impedance level, the result would show an insignificant difference across the band. Secondly, the major part of the deviations for all ratios occurs beyond 15 MHz (the effect of standing waves). Finally, the higher ratios should *never* be used to match 50 ohms to 450 ohms, 288 ohms, and 200 ohms, respectively. The characteristic impedances and choking reactances *do not* allow for broadband operation under these conditions.

Sec 15.2.2   A Low-power 5-Ratio Unun

Photo 15-C shows a low-power unit mounted in a homemade 2 inch long by 1.5 inch wide by 2.25 inch

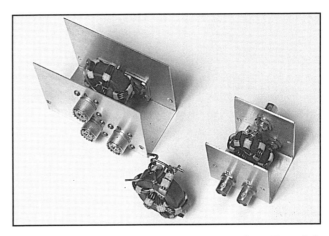

Photo 15-D. *The three 5-ratio Ununs together. From left to right, the high-power unit mounted and unmounted, the low-power unit.*

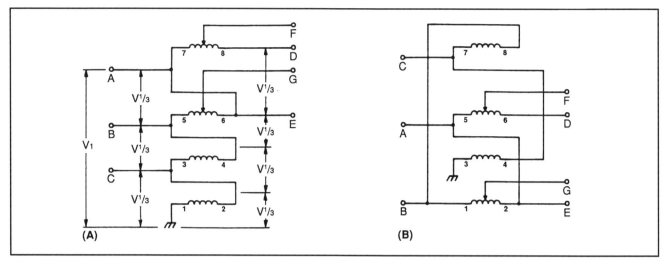

Figure 15-2. *Circuit diagrams for the 10-ratio Unun: (A) diagram for analysis; (B) transposed windings for best overall performance.*

high minibox. It has six trifilar turns of No. 16 H Thermaleze wire on a 1.25-inch OD ferrite toroid with a permeability of 250. The tap on winding 5-6 is located three turns from terminal 5, yielding ratios of 6.25:1 and 1.56:1 instead of the 5.75:1 and 1.44:1 ratios of the high-power unit. In actual use, these differences should be negligible.

Because this Unun has shorter transmission lines than its high-power counterpart, the deviations of the ratios across the band are even smaller. It is also interesting to note that, if No. 14 H Thermaleze wire was used in winding 3-4, this very small Unun could very well be rated at 500 watts of continuous power!

Photo 15-D shows all three 5-ratio Ununs together.

Sec 15.3   The 10-Ratio Unun— The Ultimate Multimatch

Figure 15-2A is presented here because it is the easiest form of a quadrifilar-wound Unun to explain. With the input voltage, V_1, connected to the various terminals on the left (the low-impedance side), and with very short transmission lines compared to the wavelength, we have the following transformation ratios:

1. V_1 connected to terminal A
   a) At terminal D the output voltage V_o is $4/3V_1$. Therefore, the transformation ratio, g, with connection A-D is:

$$g = (4/3)^2 = 1:1.78 \qquad \text{(Eq 15-5)}$$

b) At terminal F the output voltage is:

$$V_o = V_1(1 + n/3N) \qquad \text{(Eq 15-6)}$$

where:
N = total number of turns
n = number of turns from terminal 7.

The transformation ratio with connection A-F then becomes:

$$g = (V_o/V_1)^2 = (1 + n/3N)^2 \qquad \text{(Eq 15-7)}$$

2. V_1 connected to terminal B
   a) At terminal E the output voltage is $3/2V_1$. Thus, the transformation ratio with connection B-E is:

$$g = (3/2)^2 = 1:2.25 \qquad \text{(Eq 15-8)}$$

b) At terminal G the output voltage is:

$$V_o = V_1(1 + n/2N) \qquad \text{(Eq 15-9)}$$

where n = number of turns from terminal 5.

The transformation ratio with connection B-G becomes:

$$g = (V_o/V_1)^2 = (1 + n/2N)^2 \qquad \text{(Eq 15-10)}$$

c) At terminal D the output voltage is $2V_1$. The transformation ratio with connection B-D is:

$$g = (2)^2 = 1:4 \qquad \text{(Eq 15-11)}$$

d) At terminal F the output voltage is:

$$V_o = V_1(3/2 + n/2N) \qquad \text{(Eq 15-12)}$$

where n = number of turns from terminal 7.

The transformation ratio with connection B-F, then, is:

$$g = (V_o/V_1)^2 = (3/2 + n/2N) \qquad \text{(Eq 15-13)}$$

3. V_1 connected to terminal C

a) At terminal E, the output voltage is $3V_1$. The transformation ratio with connection C-E becomes:

$$g = (3)^2 = 1{:}9 \qquad \text{(Eq 15-14)}$$

b) At terminal G, the output voltage is:

$$V_o = V_1(2 + n/N) \qquad \text{(Eq 15-15)}$$

where n = number of turns from terminal 5.

The transformation ratio with connection C-G is:

$$g = (V_o/V_1)^2 = (2 + n/N)^2 \qquad \text{(Eq 15-16)}$$

c) At terminal D, the output voltage is $4V_1$. The transformation with connection C-D becomes:

$$g = (4)^2 = 1{:}16 \qquad \text{(Eq 15-17)}$$

d) At terminal F the output voltage is:

$$V_o = V_1(3 + n/N) \qquad \text{(Eq 15-18)}$$

where n = number of turns from terminal 7.

The transformation ratio with connection C-F is:

$$g = (V_o/V_1)^2 = (3 + n/N)^2 \qquad \text{(Eq 15-19)}$$

Sec 15.3.1   A High-power 10-Ratio Unun

Figure 15-2B evolved after several attempts at re-arranging the windings of **Figure 15-2A** for best over-all performance (optimizing the effective characteristic impedances of the windings). **Photo 15-E** shows the bottom view of an unmounted Unun using the circuit of **Figure 15-2B**. The top-left lead is terminal E. The top-right lead is terminal D. The bottom-left lead is terminal B. The center lead (connected to the SO-239 connector) is terminal A.

Photo 15-E. *Bottom view of the 10-ratio Unun. The connector is on terminal A.*

Photo 15-F. *Three different views of the 10-ratio Unun mounted in a 4 inch long by 2 inch wide by 2.75 inch high CU-3015A minibox.*

Photo 15-G. *The low-power unit mounted in a homemade 2.25 inch long by 1.5 inch wide by 2.25 inch high minibox.*

The bottom-right lead is terminal C. Below these three bottom leads is a ground connection (terminal 3 in **Figure 15-2B** to the SO-239 connector. **Photo 15-F** shows three different views of this high-power unit mounted in a 4 inch long by 2 inch wide by 2.75 inch high CU-3015A minibox.

This 10-ratio Unun has four quadrifilar turns of No. 14 H Thermaleze wire on a 1.5-inch OD ferrite toroid with a permeability of 250. Winding 5-6 is tapped at 2 turns from terminal 5 and winding 7-8 is tapped at 2 turns from terminal 7.

If the 9:1 ratio (connection C-E), the 12.25:1 ratio (connection C-F), and the 16:1 ratio (connection C-D), are to be used at the full legal limit of amateur radio power, then I suggest that winding 3-4 be replaced with No. 12 H Thermaleze wire. If not, then these three ratios should be used at lower power levels (of 500 watts continuous and 1 kW peak). It should also be mentioned that using No. 12 wire for winding 3-4 adds a greater degree of *difficulty* to the construction process.

A listing of the expected performance across the band from 1.7 to 30 MHz, with the various ratios, is as follows:

16:1 (D-C); 50:3.125 ohms
  Ratio is constant up to 21 MHz. It then decreases by 15 percent.
12.25:1 (F-C); 50:4.08 ohms
  Ratio is constant.
9:1 (E-C); 50:5.56 ohms
  Ratio increases by 5 percent.
6.25:1 (G-C); 50:8 ohms
  Ratio is constant.
4:1 (D-B); 50:12.5 ohms
  Ratio decreases by 5 percent.

3.06:1 (F-B); 50:16.3 ohms
  Ratio decreases by 10 percent.
2.25:1
a) (E-B); 50:22.22 ohms
  Ratio increases by 4 percent.
b) (B-E); 50:112.5 ohms
  Ratio increases by 50 percent (the greatest deviation across the band of any of the ratios).
1.78:1
a) (D-A); 50:28.1 ohms.
  Ratio is constant.
b) (A-D); 50:89 ohms.
  Ratio increases by 15 percent.
1.56:1
a) (G-B); 50:32 ohms
  Ratio increases by 10 percent.
b) (B-G); 50:78 ohms
  Ratio increases by 40 percent.
1.36:1
a) (F-A); 50:36.8 ohms
  Ratio decreases by 9 percent.
b) (A-F); 50:68 ohms
  Ratio increases by 1.5 percent.

Sec 15.3.2   A Low-power 10-Ratio Unun

Photo 15-G shows a low-power unit mounted in a homemade 2.25 inch long by 1.5 inch wide by 2.25 inch high minibox. It has five quadrifilar turns of No. 16 H Thermaleze wire on a 1.25-inch OD ferrite toroid with a permeability of 250. The tap on winding 5-6 (**Figure 15-2B**) is at three turns from terminal 5 and on winding 1-2; it is three turns from terminal 1. Because the number of turns is different from the high-power unit, so are the ratios that use the taps. In this case, they are a little larger. Specifically, the tapped ratios are now: 1:12.96, 1:6.76, 1:3.24, 1:1.69, and 1:1.44. If the taps were at two turns from terminals 5 and 1, the ratios would be a little less than those of the high-power unit. You can play with the equations in the first section of this chapter and arrive at many different ratios.

Because this Unun has shorter transmission lines than its high-power counterpart, the deviations of the ratios across the HF band are generally smaller. Also, if winding 3-4 (in **Figure 15-2B**) were replaced with No. 14 H Thermaleze wire, this low-power unit could very well be rated at 500 watts of continuous power for all ratios!

Chapter 16

Ununs for Beverage Antennas

Section 16.1   Introduction

The Beverage antenna[19] is well known by 160-meter enthusiasts for enhanced signal-to-noise ratios when there are high levels of interference and atmospheric noise. If erected properly, Beverages also have excellent directivity. However, they are quite inefficient and, therefore, not generally suitable as transmitting antennas. Important considerations with Beverages are the terminating resistor (for the more common single-wire version) and the input matching Unun (unbalanced-to-unbalanced transformer). The terminating resistor and the impedance ratio of the Unun are determined by the characteristic impedance of the antenna acting as a long transmission line with one good conductor and one poor conductor (the earth). This line is generally between 400 and 600 ohms, and theoretically given by:

$$Z_o = 138 \times \log(4h/d) \qquad \text{(Eq 16-1)}$$

where:
Z_o = characteristic impedance of the Beverage
h = height of the wire above ground
d = diameter of the wire.

This chapter presents low- and high-power versions of multimatch Ununs designed to match 50-ohm cable to unbalanced loads from 450 to 800 ohms. The low-power unit, which is capable of handling continuous power levels up to 100 watts, is specifically designed for the Beverage antenna when it is performing as a receiving antenna. The high-power unit, which is capable of handling 1 kW of continuous power, can be used with the Beverage or any other traveling wave antenna when used as a transmitting antenna. Also presented are high-power designs capable of flat response, including the entire AM broadcast band. These multimatch Ununs could be of interest to designers of high-power amplifiers for the broadcast band. A little theory on how these devices are designed is also provided.

Sec 16.2   A Little Theory

Transmission line transformers[2] (the Unun being a subset thereof) are known for having greater bandwidths and efficiencies than their counterparts, the conventional transformers. Design considerations for the two types of transformers are also vastly different. Transmission line transformers use chokes and transmission lines, while conventional transformers use flux linkages.

High-impedance Ununs (and Baluns), which match 50 ohms unbalanced to impedances as high as 800 ohms, lie at about the edge of this technology's capability. The reasons are: 1) the windings require more turns because higher reactances are needed for isolating the input from the output, and 2) they require higher characteristic impedances in the transmission lines because the loads they see are greater. Therefore, when winding one of these devices, you'll *just* run out of space on your toroidal cores when trying to satisfy the low frequency and high frequency objectives. Incidentally, beaded transmission lines are not recommended at these impedance levels because of their excessive losses.

There are two methods for obtaining broadband operation at these high impedance levels. One uses Guanella's 9:1 and 16:1 Baluns, which are converted to Unun operation.[2] The other uses higher-order windings (quadrifilar in this case) on a single core, which is an extension of Ruthroff's bootstrap approach.[2] The Guanella approach, which uses coiled transmission line connected in series at the high-impedance side and in parallel at the low-impedance side, results in very broad bandwidths—but with difficulty in meeting low-frequency objectives. Low-frequency models[2] show that, with ratios above 4:1,

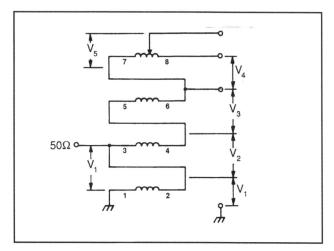

Figure 16-1. *Schematic diagram of the quadrifilar design, using Ruthroff's approach for high-impedance, low-frequency Ununs like the Beverage matching transformer.*

Photo 16-A. *The bottom view of the low-power Beverage antenna Unun.*

some of the coiled windings are connected in parallel, resulting in reduced reactances. However, with the Ruthroff approach, all of the inductances (at the low-frequency end) end up mutually aiding each other. However, Ruthroff's approach suffers at the high-frequency end because a direct voltage is summed with three voltages that traverse various lengths of transmission lines. As a result, Guanella's approach of summing voltages of equal delays is preferred for the higher frequency bands, and Ruthroff's approach is most often used for the lower frequency bands. This chapter presents designs using Ruthroff's approach.

Figure 16-1 shows the schematic diagram of a quadrifilar-wound Unun. If the lengths of the transmission lines are very short compared to the wavelength (therefore, phase delay and standing waves are negligible), then:

$$V_1 = V_2 = V_3 = V_4 \qquad \text{(Eq 16-2)}$$

at terminal 6,

$$V_o = V_1 + V_2 + V_3 = 3V_1 \qquad \text{(Eq 16-3)}$$

and the impedance ratio becomes:

$$g = (V_o/V_1)^2 = 9 \qquad \text{(Eq 16-4)}$$

At terminal 8, it becomes:

$$g = 16 \qquad \text{(Eq 16-5)}$$

The voltage at the tap in winding 7-8 is:

$$\begin{aligned}
V_o &= 3V_1 + V_5 \\
&= 3V_1 + n/NV_1 = V_1(3 + n/N) \\
&= V_1(3 + n/N) \qquad \text{(Eq 16-6)}
\end{aligned}$$

where:
N = total number of turns
n = number of turns from terminal 7

The impedance ratio, using the tapped winding, becomes:

$$g = (V_o/V_1)^2 = (3 + n/N)^2 \qquad \text{(Eq 16-7)}$$

When the lengths of the transmission lines are significant, then important phase delays can occur and reduce the high frequency response. As you can see in **Figure 16-1**, V_2 travels one transmission line, V_3 travels two transmission lines, and V_4 travels three transmission lines. Additionally, the high frequency response is further diminished if the characteristic impedances of the transmission lines are not at their optimum values (which is hard to do at these impedances levels). Even with these major flaws, the Ruthroff approach is better for Beverage antenna use because this antenna's greatest advantages are on the lower frequency bands (80 and 160 meters).

Sec 16.3   A Low-power Design

Photo 16-A shows the bottom view of a 5-turn quadrifilar-wound Unun designed to handle 100 watts of continuous power with constant ratios from 9:1 to 16:1 in the 40- and 80-meter bands. It uses the Ruthroff approach of **Figure 16-1** and is shown here to give the reader a method for making the various interconnections. For operation on the 80- and 160-meter bands, I would use 6 quadrifilar turns on a 1.5-

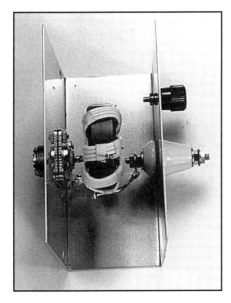

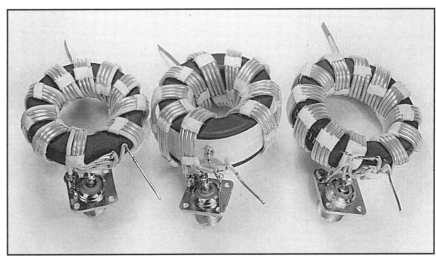

Photo 16-C. *Three high-power, low-frequency Ununs using a quadrifilar design with Ruthroff's approach. The one on the left is designed to cover the 80- and 160-meter bands. The other two are designed to cover the 160-meter and AM broadcast bands.*

Photo 16-B. *The low-power Beverage antenna Unun mounted in a 4 inch long by 2 inch wide by 2.75 inch high minibox.*

inch OD ferrite toroid with a permeability of 250. The bottom winding is No. 20 hook-up wire and the other three are No. 22 hook-up wire. Winding 7-8 is tapped at 2 turns from terminal 7, yielding a 11.11:1 ratio, and at 3 turns from terminal 7, yielding a 12.25:1 ratio. Therefore, with outputs also at terminals 6 and 8, this Unun matches 50-ohm cable to loads of 450, 555.6, 612.5, and 800 ohms.

Photo 16-B shows the unit mounted in a 4 inch long by 2 inch wide by 2.75 inch high minibox. The output (the feedthrough insulator) is connected to one of the taps. A grounded binding post is also shown.

Sec 16.4 High-power Designs

Photo 16-C shows three high-power designs. The one on the left is specifically designed to cover the frequencies generally used with traveling wave structures like the Beverage antenna. This design has 10 quadrifilar turns on a 2.4-inch OD ferrite toroid with a permeability of 250. Winding 1-2 is No. 14 tinned copper wire, and the other three are No. 16 tinned copper wire. The wires are also covered with Teflon sleeving. Winding 7-8 is tapped at 5 turns from terminal 7, yielding a ratio of 12.25:1. When matching 50-ohm cable to loads of 450 ohms (terminal 6), 612.5 ohms (the tap), and 800 ohms (terminal 8), the

variation in response is less than 5 percent from 1.5 to 4 MHz. At 6.5 MHz, the variation (which is an increase in the impedance ratio) increases to about 20 percent. **Photo 16-D** attempts to provide a better view of the connections.

The other two high-power Ununs in **Photo 16-C** are specifically designed to cover the broadcast and 160-meter bands. The one in the center has 9 quadrifilar turns (of the same wires as above) on a stack of two 2.4-inch OD ferrite toroids with permeabilities of 250. The tap on winding 7-8 is now at 4 turns from terminal 7, yielding a ratio of 11.86:1. When matching 50-ohm cable to 450 ohms (terminal 6), 593 ohms (the tap), or 800 ohms (terminal 8), the response is literally

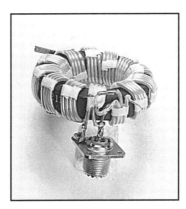

Photo 16-D. *The bottom view of the high-power Beverage antenna Unun.*

flat from 0.5 to 2 MHz. At 4 MHz, the ratios increase by about 6 percent. At 7 MHz, they increase by about 20 percent.

The Unun on the right in **Photo 16-C** illustrates another way of obtaining the same performance as above. In this case, the design has 12 quadrifilar turns (of the same wires as above) on a 2.68-inch OD ferrite with a permeability of 290. The tap on winding 7-8 is at 6 turns from terminal 7, yielding a 12.25:1 ratio (instead of 11.86:1 as above). Although the performance of this design is practically the same as the one above (using the two 2.4-inch OD cores), it is a much more expensive design because the 2.68-inch OD core is not nearly as popular. However, if a broadband, high-power and high-impedance Unun (or Balun) is required to cover 1.5 to 30 MHz, then these expensive 2.68-inch OD ferrite cores are very likely the *only* alternative!

Chapter 17

Concluding Remarks

Sec 17.1 Introduction

As I've often said, there is little information that deals with aspects of design and applications of practical hardware. Most companies are reluctant to publish their results for fear of giving away their hard-earned secrets. Textbooks only contain a few paragraphs on the subject. Therefore, very few people fully understand this technology, and, as a result, it is still far from reaching its full potential.

This book not only contains my designs, which have appeared in series written for *CQ* and *Communications Quarterly*, but also my views on other articles that have appeared in the amateur radio literature.

In the process of converting and combining the articles into appropriate chapters, one section in my article in the *CQ*, March 1993 issue entitled "Dual-Ratio Ununs," stood out as having broader applications. It is entitled "Reflections on Power Ratings" and is presented here. This information is followed by a section on misconceptions and one on the "state of the art."

After reading this book, some might think I was overly critical and didn't agree with any of the designs or explanations (or both) presented in the amateur radio literature. This is quite true. In taking this stand, I was hoping to provoke, in return, critical comment on my work. In this way, we can help our amateur friends—and perhaps even our professional friends—by advancing the understanding and application of these very useful transformers.

Sec 17.2 Reflections on Power Ratings

Power rating is one of the most controversial and least understood specifications for the transmission line transformer. As of today, no professional group has yet set the standard for this specification (as well as any other) for this popular class of matching trans-

formers. In fact, manufacturers of ferrites, which are mainly the materials used with these devices, only specify them for their uses as conventional transformers and inductors, or microwave devices.

It is well known that power ratings for practically all conventional devices are based upon catastrophic failures (usually exceeding a voltage or current limit), and failures over a relatively short period of time due to an excessive rise in temperature.

With transmission line transformers, there are really two catastrophic-type failures that can occur. One is voltage breakdown. If the device is misterminated with a high impedance (especially an open circuit), a breakdown of the insulation can occur. This is particularly true of the 1:1 Balun (50:50 ohms) that is terminated with the very high impedance of a full-wave dipole or inverted V. Using heavily coated wires (but still maintaining a characteristic impedance close to 50 ohms), or small but high-power coaxial cable, can help under these conditions.

The second catastrophic failure occurs at the low-frequency end of the transformer's passband, when the energy is not completely transmitted to the output circuit by a transmission line mode. This takes place when the reactance of the coiled or beaded transmission line is not sufficient to prevent conventional transformer currents or shunting currents to ground. Under these conditions, harmful flux can take place in the core or beads. Nonlinearities can also occur if the flux becomes appreciable. The objective in design at the low-frequency end is to have a margin of safety such that, with a termination of about three times (hence VSWR of 3:1) that of a matched condition,[2] no flux will appear in the core or beads.

The failure due to an excessive rise in temperature is the least understood of the two because it involves the failure mechanism in transmission line transformers when only transmission line currents are allowed to flow. Unlike the conventional transformer whose losses are current dependent (wire, eddy current, and hystereis losses), the transmission line transformer's losses are voltage dependent (a dielectric-type). That is, the greater the voltage drop along the length of the transmission lines, the greater the loss. Furthermore, it can be shown that only low-permeability ferrites (less than 300) yield the extremely high efficiencies of which these transformers are capable.[2]

Because all transmission line transformers have voltage drops along their transmission lines, we must look at their high-frequency models to determine the magnitude of these drops and, hence, the temperature rise that can be expected. Here are some examples:

If V_1 is the voltage that appears on the 50-ohm side of the transformer, then:

1) For a quintufilar-wound Unun, the longitudinal voltage-drop is $V_1/5$ in matching to lower impedances (like 32 or 18 ohms) and $V_1/4$ in matching to higher impedances (like 78 or 139 ohms).

2) For a quadrifilar-wound Unun, the longitudinal voltage-drop is $V_1/4$ in matching to lower impedances (like 12.5 or 28 ohms) and $V_1/3$ in matching to higher impedances (like 89 or 200 ohms).

3) For a trifilar-wound Unun, the longitudinal voltage-drop is $V_1/3$ in matching to lower impedances (like 22.22 or 25 ohms) and $V_1/2$ in matching to higher impedances (like 100 or 112.5 ohms).

4) For a bifilar-wound Unun, the longitudinal voltage-drop is $V_1/2$ in matching to a lower impedance of 12.5 ohms and V_1 in matching to a higher impedance of 200 ohms.

Because the quintufilar-wound Unun has the lowest voltage drop, it is expected to have the highest efficiency. Furthermore, it can be seen that the highest efficiencies occur in matching to lower impedances. Very accurate measurements[2] have shown that 4:1 Ununs, using ferrite cores with permeabilities of 125, have exhibited losses of only 0.02 to 0.04 dB in matching 50 to 12.5 ohms from 1 MHz to over 30 MHz. Even though the Ununs in this book have mostly used permeabilities of 250, and should have slightly greater losses, many use higher-order windings (trifilar, quadrifilar, and quintufilar) and, hence, have lower longitudinal voltage drops. Therefore, they should have losses of only 0.02 to 0.04 dB, as well.

When matching at the 1 kW level, the figures above mean that only 5 to 10 watts would be dissipated in the Unun. As a heatsink, these small transformers should be able to handle this loss easily. In fact, they should be able to handle several times this level of continuous power. Also, because they use heavily coated wires, their peak power ratings should be greater by more than a factor of two!

Another important power rating consideration is to determine what happens when the transformers are misterminated. Because the losses being considered now are dielectric-types and, hence, voltage-dependent, the harmful terminations are greater than that for which the transformers were designed. For example, if the termination is three times greater (a VSWR of 3:1), the voltages along the transmission lines would increase by a factor of 1.73. This means the losses would practically double. The Ununs described in this series, when matching to impedances lower than 50 ohms, should easily handle this mismatch. Obviously, mismatches in the range of 10:1 would result in much lower efficiencies and should be avoided.

The analysis of the losses in Baluns follows the same pattern. The voltages are as follows: under matched conditions for a 1:1 Balun (50:50 ohms), $V_1/2$; for a 4:1 Balun (50:200 ohms), V_1; for a 9:1 Balun (50:450 ohms), $1.5V_1$; and for higher-impedance Baluns it could be $2V_1$. The higher voltage drops, together with high VSWRs, means that high-impedance Baluns (and Ununs) have more loss and require larger structures to dissipate the heat. It should also be pointed out that there is a tradeoff in efficiency for low-frequency response with Baluns (and Ununs) when matching 50 ohms to higher impedances like 200 ohms, 300 ohms, 450 ohms, and higher. This is done by using permeabilities of 125 and lower.

Finally, I thought it might be useful to give some general guidelines as to what efficiencies you might expect with Baluns and Ununs when using ferrite cores or beads with a permeability of 250. Here are some expected efficiencies when matching 50 ohms to various loads under matched conditions:

Loads	Efficiency
50 ohms or less	98 to 99.5 percent
50 to 100 ohms	97 to 98 percent
100 to 200 ohms	96 to 97 percent
200 ohms and above	93 to 96 percent

As I mentioned earlier, these efficiencies would be reduced by a percent or two with a VSWR of 3:1, which increases the loss by a factor of about two. Also, the efficiencies can be increased by a percent or two with high-impedance loads (greater than 100 ohms) by resorting to lower permeability ferrites that trade off efficiency for low-frequency response. In closing, I would like to say that high-permeability manganese-zinc ferrites should be avoided because of their much higher losses. Furthermore, their losses are highly frequency dependent, while low-permeability nickel-zinc ferrites are not.

Sec 17.3   Misconceptions

From recent discussions on the air and phone calls concerning Baluns, I think the most *expensive* misconception regarding Baluns is the assumption that a 9:1 (450:50 ohm) Balun would match 50-ohm cable (or the output of a linear or transceiver) to 450-ohm twin lead, without considering the effect of its termination. In truth, the 9:1 Balun would *only* see 450 ohms if the line were terminated in 450 ohms. In reality, if the line were terminated in a 50-ohm dipole, the Balun would see 50 ohms when the line is a half-wave long and 4050 ohms when is a quarter-wave long. The 9:1 Balun is clearly useless in this application.

By far, most misconceptions regarding Baluns are due to the many radio amateurs who perceive these devices as conventional transformers that transmit the energy from input to output by flux linkages and not as transmission line transformers, which transmit energy by an efficient transmission line mode. This is clearly shown by the writers who have compared their "new" coaxial cable (coiled about a toroid or threaded through ferrite beads) Baluns with Baluns using wire transmission lines coiled about a ferrite rod or toroid. They claim their Baluns are better because the others: 1) were limited by leakage inductance, 2) did not exhibit true 1:1 impedance transformations, 3) were prone to core saturation, 4) added a reactive component to the input impedance, 5) were susceptible to unbalanced and mismatched loads, and more importantly, 6) had *more* loss.

If the writers had accepted the correct model for these devices (given to us by Guanella and Ruthroff), which shows that they are really chokes (lumped elements) and configurations of transmission lines (distributed elements), then there are several parameters they should have considered in their comparisons. They are: 1) the characteristic impedances and lengths of the transmission lines (the high-frequency capability), 2) what form of the 1:1 Balun or 4:1 Balun is used by the other Balun, 3) the low-frequency capabilities (safety margins), 4) power capabilities, and finally 5) efficiencies.

Now, had the writers used the proper parameters in their comparisons, they would have found that mismatch loss was mistaken for real (ohmic) loss; high-frequency response was limited by standing waves, and not leakage inductance or shunting capacitance; the beaded-coax Balun had *more* loss than a well-designed Balun using wire or coax transmission lines coiled about a toroid; and that their comparisons were made with either the trifilar (voltage) 1:1 Balun or the Ruthroff 4:1 Balun, which are inferior designs.

In fact, the perception that the transmission line transformer is actually a conventional transformer is so prevalent, that a new name for this class of devices should be considered—*broadband transmission line matching networks*. This name (without the word *transformer*) would help in dispelling inaccurate perceptions and in standardizing the schematic diagrams. It would place the coiled or beaded transmission lines (in the high-frequency models) horizontally, and eliminate the phasing or polarity dots.

Sec 17.4   The State of the Art

Until very recently, the radio amateur had only two types of Baluns available in the literature and on the market. They were the so-called 1:1 and 4:1 "voltage" Baluns. As was shown in **Chapter 7**, the comparisons by others with new 1:1 designs using coaxial cable (called "current" Baluns) were made with an inferior trifilar-wound Balun, instead of Ruthoff's design that appeared in his 1959 paper and became the industry's standard. Ruthroff's third conductor on his 1:1 Balun was on a separate part of the toroid, thus giving it practically the same characteristics as the Guanella ("current") Balun. These articles on newer designs not only gave a new language to our Baluns, but also presented questionable statements regarding their performances. It would be interesting if the authors of these articles compared their Baluns with well-designed Ruthroff or Guanella Baluns using 50-ohm bifilar windings or coaxial cables on low-loss ferrite toroids (less than 300 permeability). I am quite sure their claims would be greatly diminished.

As was noted in **Chapter 8**, the 4:1 voltage Balun appeared in the amateur radio journals about 25 years ago (the same time as the "inferior" 1:1 voltage Balun). Considerable design information appeared in the handbooks of the time regarding the construction and performance of this Balun. Furthermore, this information also stayed the same over these many years. As was shown in **Chapter 8**, the design was found lacking. However, with some rather simple changes, like doubling the cross-sectional area of the core, increasing the number of turns from 10 to 14, and using extra insulation on the wires to increase the characteristic impedance of the coiled transmission line from about 50 to 100 ohms (the objective), a much better design emerged. In fact, for balanced antenna systems, this new design might well be described as "peerless."

A 4:1 Guanella (current) Balun has now appeared in our handbooks. This more flexible Balun uses two transmission lines wound on separate cores and connected in series at one end and in parallel on the other. Literally, no design information is given on its construction. What is offered are recommendations for the permeability of the ferrite cores. Values from 850 to 2500 are proposed. However, use of these high permeabilities would result in lossy Baluns.

I also found it interesting, in my work on these devices, that the classic papers of Guanella[3] and Ruthroff[9] are still the cornerstones of this technology known as *transmission line transformers*. To be sure, some of us have extended the work of these two by using better measuring equipment, creating more complicated configurations, and finding new applications. However, it is apparent from the articles published in the amateur radio journals and discussions on the air and at club meetings that most radio amateurs still perceive these devices as conventional transformers. They don't look at these devices as Guanella and Ruthroff did—as chokes and transmission lines. As a result, there has been a lack of good design information in our literature.

There are many new and useful designs possible with this technology, as discussed in **Part I** of this book. They include: higher power levels, applications on the VHF and UHF bands and above, and new Baluns and Ununs with ratios other than $1:n^2$ where n = 1, 2, 3, . . . , etc. This book presents some

designs* and suggestions for higher-power and higher-frequency applications.

I see two reasons for the lack of emergence in this technology. They are:

1) This subject is not adequately covered in any college textbook, and it generally has not been of interest to academics who rightfully view their role as basic research and not applications. As a result, there are few graduates with any skill in the design of transmission line transformers—in contrast to the areas of transmission line, waveguide, and antenna theory.

2) The professional societies don't receive enough application papers. Although much of the research and development work performed in industry is highly innovative, important to the advancement of the technology, and certainly publishable in scientific journals, corporations are often reluctant to allow publication for fear of "aiding" their competition. It has been stated[29] that in the past few decades, the submission of application papers to the technical journals of the IEEE has declined. In fact, a survey by one of the technical societies showed that 85 percent of the submissions now come from universities, not industry!

In order to assist technologies, like *transmission line transformers*, which are far from reaching their potential applications, IEEE has instituted a program called *Emerging Practices in Technology* (EPT). The object of the EPT program is to facilitate the development of new standards by disseminating and making available various EPT papers to the broadest possible audience worldwide. The papers on practices in various areas of technology are peer reviewed by relevant IEEE Technical Committees, and have the potential for standardization in the future. The papers (mine is **Reference 30**) are published by the IEEE Standards Press.

FOOTNOTE

*Kits and finished units available from Amidon Associates, Inc., 240 Briggs Ave., Costa Mesa, CA 92626.

References

1. Jerry Sevick, W2FMI, *Transmission Line Transformers*, 1st edition, Amateur Radio Relay League, 1987.

2. Jerry Sevick, W2FMI, *Transmission Line Transformers*, 4th edition, Noble Publishing Corporation, 2001.

3. G. Guanella, "Novel Matching Systems for High Frequencies," *Brown-Boveri Review*, Volume 31, September 1944, pages 327–329.

4. Walt Maxwell, W2DU, "Some Aspects of the Balun Problem," *QST*, March 1983, pages 38–40.

5. John Belrose, VE2CU, "Transforming the Balun," *QST*, June 1991, pages 30–33.

6. Roy Lewallen, W7EL, "Baluns: What They Do and How They Do It," *The ARRL Antenna Compendium*, Volume 1, Amateur Radio Relay League, 1985, pages 12–15.

7. Joe Reisert, W1JR, "Simple and Efficient Broadband Balun," *Ham Radio*, September 1978, pages 12–15.

8. Richard H. Turrin, W2IMU, "Broad-Band Balun Transformers," *QST*, August 1964, pages 33–35.

9. C. L. Ruthroff, "Some Broad-Band Transformers," *Proceedings of the IRE*, Volume 47, August 1959, pages 1337–1342.

10. Richard A. Genaille, W4UW, "How to Build a Multi-Tap Unun," *CQ* May 1992, pages 28–32.

11. Bruce Eggers, WA9NEW, "An Analysis of the Balun," *QST*, April 1980, pages 19–21.

12. Richard H. Turrin, W2IMU, "Application of Broad-Band Balun Transformers," *QST*, April 1969, pages 42, 43.

13. George Badger, W6TC, "A New Class of Coaxial-Line Transformers, Part 1," *Ham Radio*, February 1980, pages 12–18.

14. George Badger, W6TC, "A New Class Of Coaxial-Line Transformers, Part 2," *Ham Radio*, March 1980, pages 18–29, 70.

15. Bill Orr, W6SAI, "Radio Fundamentals: The Coax Balun," *CQ*, November 1993, pages 60–65.

16. Albert Roehm, W2OBJ, "Some Additional Aspects of the Balun Problem," *The ARRL Antenna Compendium*, Volume 2, Amateur Radio Relay League, pages 172–174.

17. Lew McCoy, W1ICP, "Let's Talk About Wire," Part 1, *CQ*, January 1993, pages 42–45.

18. Lew McCoy, W1ICP, "Let's Talk About Wire," Part 2, *CQ*, February 1993, pages 32–42.

19. Gerald Hall, K1TD, Editor, *The ARRL Antenna Book*, 16th edition, Amateur Radio Relay League, 1991, Chapter 25.

20. George Grammer, W1DF, "Simplified Design of Impedance-Matching Networks," in three parts, *QST*, March, April, and May 1957.

21. D.K. Belcher, "RF Matching Techniques, Design and Example," *QST*, October 1972, page 24.

22. Lew McCoy, W1ICP, "The Ultimate Transmatch," *QST*, July 1970, pages 24–27, 58.

23. Warren Bruene, W5OLY, "Introducing the Series-Parallel Network," *QST*, June 1986, page 21.

24. Louis Varney, G5RV, "The G5RV Muliband Antenna...Up-to-Date," *The Antenna Compendium*, Volume 1, Amateur Radio Relay League, pages 86–90.

25. Jerry Sevick, W2FMI, "6:1 and 9:1 Baluns," *Communications Quarterly*, Winter 1993, pages 43–51.

26. D. Meyer, "Equal-Delay Networks Match Impedances Over Wide Bandwidths," *MICROWAVES & RF*, April 1990, pages 179–188.

27. S.E. London and S.V. Tomeshevich, "Line Transformers with Fractional Transformation Factor," *Telecommunications and Radio Engineering,* Volume 28/29, April 1974.

28. Carl Markle, K8IHQ, "Wideband RF Baluns," *73 Amateur Radio Today*, September, 1992, pages 20–23.

29. S. Maas, D. Hornbuckle, D. Masse, "Applications Papers for the *MTT Transactions*," Summer 1992, IEEE MTT-S Newsletter, pages 3, 5.

30. Jerry Sevick, W2FMI, "Design and Realization of Broadband Transmission Line Matching Transformer," *Emerging Practices in Technology*, IEEE Standards Press, 1993.

Index

Shaping Knitting

A DESIGNER'S GUIDE TO UNDERSTANDING STITCHES

Alison Ellen

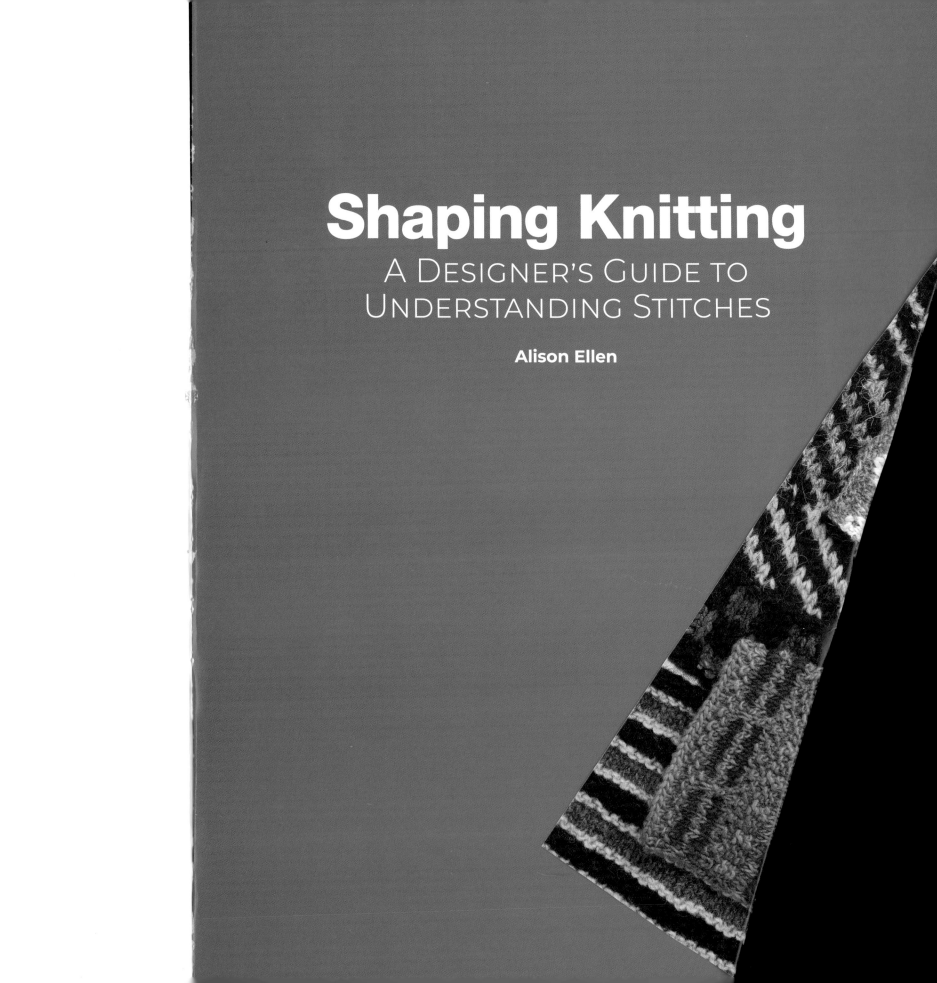